European Foundation
for the Improvement of
Living and Working Conditions

Occupational accidents and diseases
Data sources

United Kingdom

Loughlinstown House
Shankill, Co. Dublin, Ireland

THE UNIVERSITY OF NOTTINGHAM

Head of Department

PROFESSOR E. N. CORLETT
Phd DSc CEng FIProdE
FIMechE ABPsS

DEPARTMENT OF PRODUCTION ENGINEERING
AND PRODUCTION MANAGEMENT
UNIVERSITY PARK
NOTTINGHAM NG7 2RD
Telephone: 0602 506101
Telex 37346: call back UNINOT G

BIBLIOGRAPHICAL REVIEW OF

OCCUPATIONAL ACCIDENTS AND DISEASES

FOR THE UK

G.I. Johnson

J.R. Wilson

S.M. Grey

Nottingham, U.K.
April, 1985

Contract Number 84-I-1/a-4000-3

Research organisations were engaged within each State to carry out the terms of the research contract and are as follows:

Belgium	– Mr. V. Theunissens; Institute pour l'Amelioration de Conditions de Travail (IACT) Brussels.
Denmark	– Mr. D. Bunnage; Socialforskningsinstituttet, Copenhagen.
Federal Republic of Germany	– Dr. K. Kuhn; Bundesanstalt für Arbeitsschutz, Dortmund.
France	– Mdm. M. Thanh, Institut National de recherche et de Sécurite (INRS) Paris.
Greece	– Mr. N. Sarafopoulos, Consultant/Reseacher, Patra
Ireland	– Mr. C. Carroll; Institute for Industrial Research and Standards, Dublin.
Italy	– Ms. M.V. Tirone; Istituto Nazionale per l'Assicurazione contro gli Infortuni sul Lavoro (INAIL) Rome.
Luxembourg	– Mr. A. Schuster, Consultant/Reseacher, Olm
Netherlands	– Dr. R. Prinz; Stichting CCOZ, Amsterdam.
United Kingdom	– Dr. J. Wilson; University of Nottingham.

In addition to national research a contract to produce a consolidated version showing an overall comparison of the different situations in member States of the Community was awarded to Professor R. Booth and Dr. I. Glendon of Health and Safety, Technology and Management Ltd., (HASTAM) Staffordshire, England.

This present study is part of the series of bibliographical reviews and, in accordance with the guidelines, it sets out to examine present practice in four major areas sub-divided as follows:

- . reporting and notifying occupational accidents, diseases and other occurances to include legislation, criteria required in reports, statistical digests, studies of practice etc.

- compensation practice for occupational injuries and diseases, including similar material to that as above.

- information available on a few specific hazard/accident types being fatal accidents, falls from heights, noise and occupational deafness and asbestos. Information on each hazard to include details of reporting, compensation, prevention measures, inspection procedures etc.

- mortality and morbidity studies - a selective approach to published literature of significant research in the area. It addresses where possible certain specific aspects as, types of accidents and diseases, particular groups of workers, particular industrial studies, epidemological and statistical studies, specific age groups of workers, sociological, environmental and behavioural approaches etc.

All ten studies are published by the Foundation in their original language i.e. relating to the language of the country in question whereas the consolidated report is published in all seven working languages of the Community (Danish, Dutch, English, French, German, Greek and Italian). All findings expressed in these reports are the responsibility of the researchers and not of the Foundation.

The Foundation wishes to thank the researchers concerned in this study for timely and substantive reports all produced in accordance with the requirements of the Foundation and supporting a speedy publication of results.

On the 4th November 1982 the Commission of the European Communities submitted to the Council a proposal for a Council resolution on a second programme of action of the European Communities on safety and health at work. Within this proposal it was suggested that the Europoean Foundation for the Improvement of Living and Working Conditions may well have a role to play. Since the Foundation had earlier been engaged in research in health and safety, the Foundation's executive, taking the initiative from this statement in the proposal, studied more fully its terms and commenced discussion with the Commission's DG V/E/2, Health and Safety Directorate. Areas were identified in which it was considered Foundation activity would provide a useful input. These included the collection and dissemination of information at national and Community level on safety and health at work and more specifically in the development of comparable work related statistical data on mortality, accidents and resulting absenteeism attributable to sickness.

From the previous Community wide survey 'Safety and Health at the Workplace' in 1980, the Foundation had already gained valuable experience and proposed to carry out a similar study throughout all ten Member States. This to consider needs expressed by the Commission and to be in line with the Foundation's brief of being concerned about improvment of the workplace. After a number of discussions with the staff of DG V/E/2 the study was embarked upon following guidelines produced by the Foundation to meet its own requirements and extended somewhat to absorb elements required by the Commission.

The Bibliographic Review of Data Sources on Occupational Accidents and Diseases was embarked upon in December 1984; a state of the art survey of legislation, existing statistics, compensation and reporting practices required by law, and research as expressed through published sources in all ten Member States.

FOREWORD

Every effort has been made to adhere to the guidelines set out by The European Foundation document " - : Classification scheme" (January) for the draft national reports. Naturally, some flexibility in the interpretation of suggested present-ation has been necessary and there are a few exceptions to the guidance given. As far as was possible material was inc-luded under the headings and sub-headings outlined in the classification scheme in accordance with the required format. It was felt that some references were explained in sufficient detail in the text to require limited or no annotation in the bibliographies. Others are described adequately by their title alone.

The literature searched included reports, book, journals, articles, conference proceedings and official statistical and Government publications. The Health and Safety Executive's library and information services database, known commercially as HSELINE was consulted and proved to be a major help in the collation of materials.

Late Information

Since production of the draft and final versions of this rep-ort, certain publications have appeared of which the reader should be aware:

i) The U.K. Health and Safety Statistics for 1981 and 1982 have appeared (see Section 2.2). However, as stated in the body of this report, the figures are comparable neither to previous years, nor, prospectively, to future years.

HEALTH AND SAFETY EXECUTIVE. Statistics: health and safety 1981-82. London: HMSO. 1985. pp.74.

ii)   The Health and Safety Commission seem at last to have
      agreed the new basis for reporting occupational accidents
      and ill health.   There will be a new unified reporting
      arrangement for accidents causing injury, and dangerous
      occurrences.   There will also be an interim scheme of
      reporting specified ill-health conditions associated
      with particular forms of work. Draft regulations, largely
      based upon the 1983 proposals (see Section 2.1.4) should
      be implemented in early 1986. (see Ergonomics, 28/9,
      1985, p.1379.

iii) The new Asbestos (Prohibitions) Regulations (see Sections
      4.4.1 and 4.4.2) were laid before the U.K. Parliament
      in June, 1985, and will come into force on 1st January,
      1986.   Consultative comments are still being analysed
      for the proposed Control of Asbestos at Work Regulations.

iv)   A very recent report on fatalities is:

      HEALTH AND SAFETY EXECUTIVE. "Deadly maintenance - a
      study of fatal accidents at work. London: HMSO. 1985.

      Also, a further two reports were produced, as companion
      volumes, concerned with the epidemiology of accidents
      related to maintenance activities, one on roofs and the
      other with plant and machinery.

CONTENTS:

ABBREVIATIONS USED IN THE REPORT

ACA	Advisory Committee on Asbestos
APEX	Association of Professional, Executive, Clerical and Computer Staff
BNFL	British Nuclear Fuels Ltd.
BOHS	British Occupational Hygiene Society
CBI	Confederation of British Industry
CIMAH	Control of Major Accident Hazards (Regs.)
D.E.	Department of Employment
DHSS	Department of Health and Social Security
EC	European Community
EMAS	Employment Medical Advisory Service
EOC	Equal Opportunities Commission
FI	Factory Inspectorate
HASAWA	Health and Safety at Work etc. Act
HMSO	Her Majesty's Stationery Office
HSC	Health and Safety Commission
HSE	Health and Safety Executive
IIBS	Industrial Injuries Benefit Scheme
LA	Local Authorities
MRC	Medical Research Council
MSC	Manpower Services Commission
NADOR	Notification of Accidents and Dangerous Occurrences Regulations
NI	National Insurance
SI	Statutory Instrument
SIC	Standard Industrial Classification
SPAID	Society for the Prevention of Asbestos and Industrial Diseases
TLV	Threshold Limit Value
TUC	Trades Union Congress
VDU	Visual Display Unit
YTS	Youth Training Scheme

CHAPTER 1

INTRODUCTION

Royal Assent was given to the Health and Safety at Work etc. Act (HASAWA) on 31st July, 1974 and it came into force on 10th October that year. Certain provisions took effect in the early months of 1975. The HASAWA, its objectives and its administration embodies the United Kingdom's official philosophy towards health, safety and welfare of workpeople (as well as the safety and health of the general public affected by work activities). The U.K.'s approach towards occupational accidents and occupationally related diseases is an integral part of the HASAWA. Generally speaking, Britain's philosophy may be described as primarily preventative in nature and can be considered as fairly typical of health and safety attitudes in developed Western nations.

A decade later is perhaps an appropriate time to examine the changes brought about by the HASAWA. Legislation laying down minimum standards of safety, health and welfare originated in the U.K. more than one hundred years ago. Until the 1970's about sixty per cent of this country's workforce was protected by a patchwork of separate codes of law made up of almost five hundred statutory instruments with over thirty statutes.

It was in 1972 that the Robens Report [1] attempted to survey, for the first time, the whole problem of occupational health and safety in the U.K. The aim was to identify the defects in the traditional approaches to the problem, and to make recommendations for a completely new system of legislation to achieve those objectives. The Report made a series of fundamental criticisms of the early legal framework, together with suggested solutions. The 1974 Act represents Parliaments' attempt to implement both the general philosophy and the detailed recommendations of the Robens Report.

One of the main proposals of the report was the formulation

of a new philosophy for accident prevention. It was contended that there were real limitations, (with respect to health and safety standards) in the negative regulations previously adopted. The previous system had encouraged too much reliance on external regulations and too little on personal responsibility and voluntary effort. The Robens Committee believed that the primary responsibility in relation to occupational accidents and diseases lay with those who created the risks and with those who work with them. It was proposed that, although responsibility lay with employers and workers, management was in the best position to give a lead in matters of safety.

The Robens Committee was not convinced that safety and health at work could be ensured by an ever expanding body of legal regulations enforced by legal means, but it was equally convinced that the role of law remained crucial; and that this law should be simple, of general application and should be firmly enforced. The natural implications of many of the Committee's recommendations (and their eventual manifestation in the HASAWA) involve wider powers for inspection, and greater responsibilities for employers and managers than before.

To fully appreciate the state of occupational health and safety in the U.K., the background consisting of the HASAWA and its operation must be understood. Instead of making detailed provisions itself, the HASAWA gives powers to the Secretary of State for Employment, acting through the Health and Safety Commission (HSC), to draw up detailed regulations and codes of practice on specific health and safety matters. It is a broad framework which with future and existing legislation will make up the full body of health and safety legislation. A list of instruments and codes of practice issued under the HASAWA is included as Appendix 3 to this report. This was produced by HSE in mid-1985.

It is important to remember that although the HASAWA imposes many extra general duties on employers, it does not remove, cancel or affect any existing legislation such as the Factories Act, the Mines and Quarries Act, etc. These and any other pieces of legislation continue side-by-side with the HASAWA legislation. The relationship of the HASAWA and existing legislation is illustrated below:

HEALTH AND SAFETY AT WORK, etc. ACT 1974

HASAWA

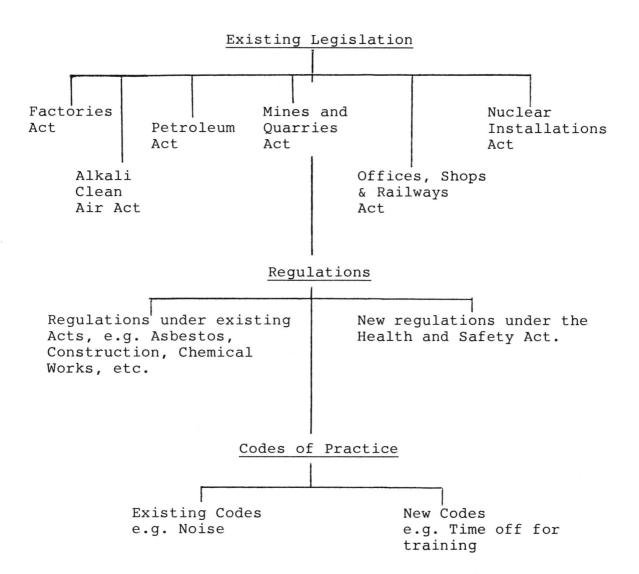

The main purpose of the HASAWA is to provide for one, comprehensive, integrated system of law. The HASAWA;

- completely overhauled and modernised the existing law dealing with safety, health and welfare at work.

- put new general duties on employers, ranging from providing and maintaining a safe place of work to consulting with workers.

- created the Health and Safety Commission (HSC).

- reorganised and unified the various Government inspectorates into a body called the Health and Safety Executive (HSE).

- provided new powers and penalties for the enforcement of safety laws.

- established methods of occupational safety and health, and ways of operating safety regulations.

The Health and Safety Commission (HSC) is made up of a full-time, independent chairman and nine part-time commissioners. The commissioners are made up of three TUC members, three CBI members, two from Local Authorities and an independent member. The HSC has taken over responsibility formerly held by various government departments for the control of most occupational safety and health matters. The commission is responsible for the Health and Safety Executive.

The former government inspectorates (such as the Factory Inspectorate, Mines and Quarries, etc.) were merged into one body now called the Health and Safety Executive (HSE). The HSE inspectors have powers at their disposal to enforce the HASAWA. The relationship between the HSC, the HSE and its various structures is illustrated below:

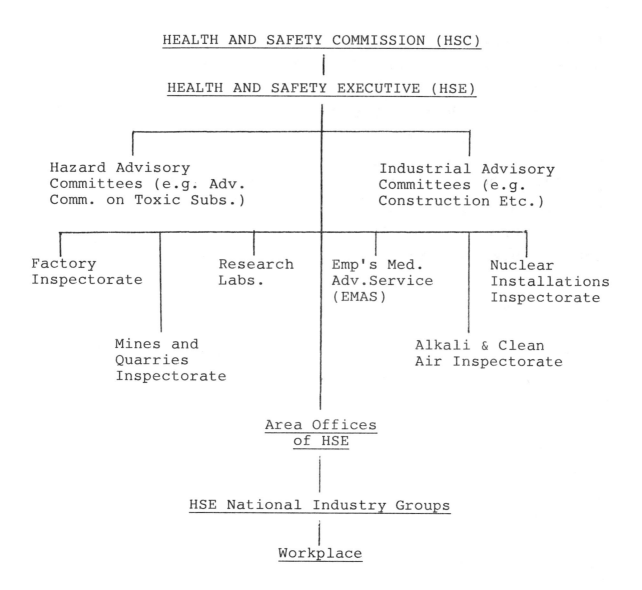

The HASAWA provided for three main systems of compulsion on employers to provide and maintain a safe and healthy place of work - improvement notices, prohibition notices and increased fines and the threat of imprisonment. The provisions of the HASAWA give comprehensive powers to the HSC to make regulations and to draw up proposals for the extension, revision or replacement of existing legislation concerning the protection of the safety and health of workpeople. However, the Act states that no changes will be made to existing statutory protection until adequate measures are available to replace them.

Most occupational health services in the U.K. owe their existence, not to the Department of Health and Social Security

(DHSS) or any other government department, but to employers themselves (both in private and nationalised industries). There are no statutory requirements for any organisation to supply medical cover other than first aid. Nevertheless, many companies do offer their employees professional occupational health services.

In 1976 the Employment Medical Advisory Service (EMAS) conducted a survey of occupational health services in the private sector of U.K. industry. Only 2.5% of firms employ both doctors and nurses. On the whole, size of workforce was likely to be more of a determining factor in whether occupational health care is provided in an organization than was the nature of the work or process, although there was greater provision in manufacturing than non-manufacturing industries. There is little evidence to suggest that this situation has been drastically altered. The growth of health services that has occurred (e.g. in smaller businesses) is probably the result of HASAWA enforcement. The HASAWA made it the duty of every employer "to ensure as far as it is reasonably practicable, the health, safety and welfare at work of his employees".

Government responsibility to occupational health lies in controlling the work environment rather than in providing medical services in the workplace. The HASAWA lays down minimum requirements for regular safety inspections of the workplace and the provision of first aiders.

At a more general level, the DHSS, Scottish Home and Health Department (SHHD), the Welsh Office, HSC and Manpower Services Commission (MSC) are represented on major international committees concerned with health, social affairs, environmental pollution and occupational safety matters. The UK follows European Community (EC) directives and normally subscribes to EC recommendations. Interchange of ideas, views and personnel with overseas countries is achieved by staff of the above departments. Within the U.K. at national government level occupational health and hygiene matters are basically the responsibility of EMAS of the HSC. EMAS took over all the medical functions of the Department of Employment group with the exception of medical examinations carried out by the regional medical services of the DHSS, SHHD and Welsh Office.

As its name implies, EMAS is basically an advisory service; the advice being freely available to doctors in occupational medicine and others. EMAS may undertake studies and research to identify an occupational health hazard. EMAS also has a number of powers designed to help them investigate hazards.

For many years the Trades Union Congress (TUC) has actively campaigned for improvements in workplace health and safety. The TUC has always been convinced that effective trade union organisation at work is the key to reducing accidents and diseases. It has pressed for and won new rights and functions for safety representatives. The TUC believes that its policy on workplace safety and health offers a prospect of real advance in accident and disease prevention. Perhaps the TUC's major influence in formulating government policy on health and safety matters is through its membership of the HSC, and the latter's formal committee structure.

The current and planned work of the HSC and the HSE, its operative arm, is outlined in the document "HSC plan of work 1985-6" [2]. In developing the plan attention has been given to trends in society and UK industry. For example, the continuing decline in primary manufacturing industry with the accompanying increase in the number of small firms, often in high technology fields, is becoming more pronounced. Obviously inspection policies will be affected. Another trend of the 1980's is the general public's increasing concern with occupational health risks and the effects on the environment and local communities of industrial activities.

The current U.K. attitude towards health and safety throughout the industrial scene has improved markedly over the last ten

years. Both management and employees have an increased awareness of the need for safe methods of working. The HSC intends
to enhance this interest to develop further the self assessment approach which underlines the HASAWA.

In recent years the resources available to the HSC have come
under scrutiny by Government, resulting in staff reduction,
an amount of re-organisation and certain policy changes.
Utilization of HSC resources is being maximised by the application of cost/benefit techniques. In fact, economic assess-
ments are now standard practice. The cost/benefit technique
applied to policy-making has come under a great deal of criticism, while the HSC anticipate that these real resources will
not be reduced significantly in the foreseeable future.

Bibliography

1. ROBENS REPORT. "Report of the Committee on Safety and
Health at Work, 1970-72" Cmnd 5034. London: HMSO 1972.

A government committee set up in response to criticisms of
the existing situation in U.K. health and safety. Its recommendations covered the mass of available safety legislation,
methods of enforcement, and remit of the law, as well as the
transfer of emphasis from technical standards to safer working
systems, and the active involvement of workers in accident
prevention. The report became the basis for the HASAWA.
Criticisms have been levelled at the report by workers' organisations, Trade Unions, and others, as the grounds of non-
applicability to many types of infringement, and its general
permissiveness (e.g. [3]).

2. HEALTH AND SAFETY COMMISSION. "Plan of Work 1985-86 and
Onwards". London: HMSO 1985. 44pp.

The (obligatory) HSC plan for their work in the future. This
covers the environment for relevant activities (employment
etc.); future resource allocation; detailed plans and objec-

tives; and analyses where the HSC and HSE should be in ten years time.

3. KINNERSLY, P.   "The Hazards of Work How to Fight Them" London: Pluto Press 1973.   394 pp.

An early but probably best regarded of the radical reviews of industrial safety and health. Much is still relevant today (see [1] above).

CHAPTER 2

REPORTING AND NOTIFYING OCCUPATIONAL ACCIDENTS, DISEASES AND OTHER OCCURRENCES

This chapter outlines the legislation and criteria for reporting occupational accidents and diseases and other occurrences for the U.K.

It should be noted these are presented in Appendix 1, in summary form. Statistical and data sources are described and recent health and safety statistics are given. (Again an associated Appendix 2 shows summarised statistics).

Contents

2.1   Legislation
2.2   Statistical information
2.3   Bibliography
2.4   Tables

2.1   Legislation

2.1.1 Introduction

In the U.K. there are obligations upon an employer to notify or report accidents that occur at work and these are supported in turn by an obligation upon any employee involved to provide details to his/her employer as soon as the accidents occur, or as soon as is practical.

An employee who suffers an injury from an accident at work must notify the employer, supervisor (or foreman) as soon as possible. If the injured person cannot do so, then a fellow employee is obliged to notify the management on behalf of the injured person. The notification need only be oral, although certain details must be given, and (at present) no such notification is required for a prescribed industrial disease. Where the employer of the injured person keeps an accident book, then entry of the required details in that book amounts to notification.

The above represents the employee's duty to report any accident, under the obligations imposed by benefit legislation. The Social Security (Claims and Payments) Regulations 1979 (SI 1979 No. 628) specify the particulars relating to a work accident which must be reported by or for an injured employee. These particulars include the full name of the employee together with full address, date, time and place of the accident and its cause and the nature of the employee's injuries. Should such details fail to be provided then there will be a delay in any claim the employee might make for industrial injuries benefit (and he/she may lose the right to benefit completely).

At every factory (as defined under the Factories Act 1961)¹, every mine or quarry, and at every other workplace where there are ten or more employees (normally employed) an accident book (form Bl 510) must be kept. The accident book must be readily accessible to the employees and other concerned persons, and must be preserved for three years after the last entry. It is important to note that this duty is quite separate from the duty to notify accidents etc. under the 1980 'Notification of Accidents and Dangerous Occurrences Regulations' (henceforth abbreviated to NADOR [4]). The regulations pertaining to the accident book are laid down in the Social Security (Claims and Payments) Regulations 1979, Reg 25. It is also incumbent upon an employer when notified of an accident at work (whether such notification be direct or through the accident book) to take reasonable steps to investigate the accident. The employer is also required to record any discrepancy between the details given and the employer's own findings.

When an employee makes a claim for industrial injuries benefit as a result of injuries suffered by an accident at work, then the employer is required by the DHSS (Department of Health and Social Security) to fill in form B176 giving details of the accident. The HSE (Health and Safety Executive) are notified in turn by the DHSS of the details of the accident.

2.1.2 NADOR

In January 1981 the NADOR (1980) [4] came into force, setting out the obligations of employers to provide information about accidents to their employees, and about dangerous occurrences, to the authorities responsible for the administration of the HASAWA (Health and Safety at Work etc Act) 1974. These regulations replaced the provisions previously contained in the Factories Act 1961 and other related legislation. The most important factor of NADOR is that they extend the scope of accident notification to virtually the whole working population. They include for the first time, for example, hospitals, schools, colleges and people at work in the fire service. Also, in some cases NADOR applies to accidents in which a member (or members) of the public is (are) injured.

They apply to the U.K. with the exception of Northern Ireland. They also apply to certain specialised work activities within territorial waters, but not to offshore installations nor to pipelines within U.K. territorial waters.

NADOR eliminated the former expensive and time-consuming system whereby accidents were required to be reported twice to different departments (the HSE and DHSS) on different forms at different times. Under the regulations a wide category of dangerous occurrences must also be notified and reported.

Under NADOR, for the purposes of notification, accidents which arise as a result of or in connection with work fall into three categories:

(1)   fatal accidents;

(2)   major injury accidents; and

(3)   accidents to employees which result in more than three
       days consecutive absence.

Only those accidents in the first two categories are
required to be reported directly (i.e. notified).
Information about those in the third category which form the
majority are received from the DHSS using the Bl 76 reporting
procedures (mentioned earlier).

A distinction is made under NADOR between notifiable and
reportable accidents. An accident is 'notifiable' if it
'arises out of or in connection with work' and with one of the
following results:

(a)   the death of or major injury to anyone, or

(b)   an employee at work being incapacitated for work for more
       than three consecutive days, excluding the day of the
       accident and any rest day.

'Arises out of or in connection with work' includes
accidents arising out of employment as well as those
incidental to it. It specifically includes an accident or
dangerous occurrence attributable to the manner of conducting
an undertaking, the plant or substances used, or to the
condition of the work premises.

A 'major injury' is defined as

-     a fracture of the skull, spine or pelvis;

-     fracture of the arm or leg bone (other than bones in the
       hands, wrist, foot and ankle);

-     amputation of the hand or foot;

-     loss of sight of an eye;

-     any other injury which results in the person injured
       being admitted into hospital as an in-patient for more
       than twenty-four hours, unless the person is detained for
       observation only.

An accident which results in a major injury and arises out of or in connection with work is 'notifiable' even though the victim is not an employee but a member of the public. Thus the law on accident reporting has extended beyond the confines of accidents to employees only.

Any dangerous occurrence which 'arises out of or in connection with work' must be notified and reported if it is of a class specified in the NADOR. The classification is in four parts depending upon where the dangerous occurrence takes place -

(I - anywhere;   II - at a mine;   III - at a quarry;   IV - on a railway)

The duty to notify and report is that where there is either:

- a notifiable accident resulting in the death of or a major injury to any person, or
- a notifiable dangerous occurrence,
then the responsible person must:

i)   immediately notify the relevant enforcing authority of the accident or occurrence by the quickest practicable means (usually by telephone); and

ii) send a written report confirming the notification on form F2508 to the same enforcing authority within seven days.

The relevant enforcing authority will be the authority responsible for enforcing the 1974 HASAWA in the particular case. The table below summarises the main examples of the authority to report to in the event of fatality, a major injury accident, or a notifiable dangerous occurrence.

Premises by main activity	To whom to report:
1. Factories and factory offices.	H.M. Factory Inspectorate
2. Mines and quarries	H.M. Mines and Quarries Inspectorate
3. Farms (and associated activites)', horticultural premises, and forestries.	H.M. Agricultural Inspectorate
4. Civil Engineering and construction sites.	H.M. Factory Inspectorate
5. Statutory and non-statutory railways.	Inspecting Officer of Railways
6. Shops, Offices, separate catering services, launderettes.	District Council (or equivalent)
7. Hospitals, Research and development', water supply postal services and telecommunications, entertainment and recreational services, local government, educational services, and road conveyance.	H.M. Factory Inspectorate

So, only work accidents (i.e. occupational accidents) resulting in the death of or major injury to a person are required by the Regulations to be notified and reported to the enforcing authority. (NADOR does not require an accident to be notified and reported to the enforcing authority, if no death or major injury results). This is because those (other) accidents where an employee is incapacitated from work for more than three days will', in any case, be reported to the DHSS under the industrial injuries benefit procedure and thence passed on to the HSE.

A notifiable accident or notifiable dangerous occurrence should be notified by a 'responsible person' who will in most cases be the employer of the person injured. However, the definition of the responsible person varies according to the workplace: the position is that a responsible person is one of the following:

- at a mine, the mine manager;
- at a quarry, the quarry owner;
- at a closed tip, the owner of the mine or quarry with which the tip is associated;
- relating to a pipeline, the owner of the pipeline;
- in other cases (apart from those above), the employer;
- in the absence of the person designated above, the person for the time being having control of the premises which the notifiable accident or the notifiable dangerous occurrence happened.

Any employer must notify the relevant enforcing authority in writing of the death of any employee occurring within one year of a notifiable accident or a notifiable dangerous occurrence.

2.1.3. Exemptions

There are a number of exceptions to notify and report laid down by the Regulations.

These exceptions are:-

i)   a self-employed person not engaged in work under the control of another, but only to a self-employed person under another's control (for example, a subcontracted electrician on a building site working for a main contractor);

ii) a patient undergoing treatment in a hospital or in the surgery of a doctor or dentist;

iii) a member of the armed forces or visiting forces who was on duty at the time of the accident.

An accident which has to be reported under one of the following provisions does not also have to be notified under the NADOR.

- the Regulations of Railways Act 1871 and Orders or Regulations thereunder;
- the Explosives Act 1875;
- the Merchant Shipping Acts 1894-1979 and Orders or Regulations made thereunder;
- the Railway Employment (Prevention of Accidents) Act 1900;
- the Nuclear Installations Act 1965 and Orders and Regulations made thereunder;
- the Ionising Radiations (Unsealed Radioactive Substances) Regulations 1968;
- the Civil Aviation (Investigation of Accidents) Regulations 1969;
- the Air Navigation (Investigation of Combined Military and Civil Air Accidents) Regulations 1969;
- the Health and Safety (Agriculture)(Bismous Substances) Regulations 1975.

In order to achieve compliance with the NADOR, records are kept that contain the following information:

a)   the date of the accident or dangerous occurrence
b)   the name, age, sex and occupation of the person involved
c)   the nature of the injury
d)   the place where the accident or dangerous occurrence took place
e)   a brief description of the circumstances

In order to achieve compliance with the Social Security (Claims and Payments) Regulations, records should be kept that contain the following information:

a)   the full name and address and occupation of the injured
     employee

b)   the date and time of the accident

c)   the place of the accident

d)   the cause and nature of the injury

e)   the name, address and occupation of the person giving
     notice of the accident, if someone other than the injured
     person.

In addition to the requirement to record details of
accidents and dangerous occurrences, the management needs
to keep written records (form F2509 or equivalent) of all
DHSS enquiries relating to claims by employees with
regard to any prescribed disease - under the Social
Security Act 1975 for the purposes of industrial injuries
benefits, or concerning pneumoconiosis or byssinosis.
Such records are to contain the following information:

-    the age, sex and occupation of the person suffering from
     the prescribed disease;

-    the nature of the disease for which the claim was made;

-    the date of first absence from work on account of the
     disease.

It should be noted that there is a need to provide
information concerning certain accidents and dangerous
occurrences (and occupational disease) to interested parties
other than the enforcing agencies. These interested parties
include:

(a) Insurance Companies
     Generally speaking they need to be notified of any
     accidents, dangerous occurrences and occupational
     diseases which are likely to result in a claim. This
     aspect is usually a condition of the insurance contract.

(b) Safety Representatives
     An employer must make available to safety representatives
     the information within the employer's knowledge necessary
     to enable them to fulfill their functions. (Safety
     Representatives and Safety Committee Regulations 1977).

(c) Trade Associations

Many trade associations require their member firms to supply them with accident information on an annual basis.

2.1.4 Proposals for new arrangements

In 1983 an HSC Consultative Document [5] was published, aiming to achieve far more than just the resurrection of an effective system of accident reporting. The proposals concerning the revision of arrangement for reporting accidents, etc. were made necessary by the loss of eighty per cent of the information received by the HSE, via the DHSS under NADOR (1980). This was one of the outcomes of the abolition of industrial injury benefit (see Chapter 3 - Compensation for Occupational Accidents and Diseases).

The proposed new arrangements involve a return to a system of direct reporting of incidents very similar to that which operated prior to 1981. Unfortunately, this would mean the re-imposition on employers of the duty to report lost-time accidents which was removed in 1981 by the NADOR. One feature of the proposed re-arrangements is that the reporting and notification systems would weave together, into a single system, reporting obligations in respect of four types of incident:

- major injuries and fatalities;
- dangerous occurrences;
- lost-time accidents;
- acute and chronic ill-health known to be associated with work.

The notification of cases of occupational diseases (and work-related chronic ill-health) was not covered by the 1980 Regulations.

Other notable features of the proposals are:

- a single report form would be used for supplying all the information demanded of employers relating to both ill-health and incidents;

- self-employed persons would, for the first time, be required to report major injuries and lost-time accidents which happened to them at their own premises;

- the reporting of lost-time accidents to trainees should be covered; and

- a procedure would be established whereby the HSE could request additional information on reported incidents.

There is no firm recommendation in the proposals as to what criteria should be used to determine when a lost-time accident has to be reported. Instead, two alternatives are put forward. One is that accidents would need to be reported if they caused absences from work of more than three days; the other that the duty to report accidents would be limited to those resulting in more than seven days absence.

At present, the NADOR (1980) are still in use and proposals for a changed system remain just that. In fact, the situation is not at all clear. This is partially due to the changeable nature of Social Security legislation, and the industrial injuries benefits scheme in particular.

As was noted earlier, under the NADOR employers must keep records of all accidents resulting in absences of more than three days. Concern that a move to a seven day criterion for reporting accidents might lead employers to feel that there was no need for them to record less serious accidents underlies a third option put forward in the proposals: that a move to an over-7-day reporting criterion would be accompanied by a requirement that details of accidents resulting in absences of more than three days would nevertheless still have to be 'recorded' by employers or other "responsible persons".

It is obvious that the introduction of a facility whereby HSE could demand more detailed information about particular reported accidents would compensate for the loss of data which would result from the adoption of an over-seven-day reporting criterion.

At present, there are only very limited requirements concerning the reporting of cases of occupational ill-health (i.e. diseases etc.). Under the NADOR employers are only required to notify cases of acute ill-health attributable to the inhalation of or ingestion of substances or to exposure to pathogens. They are also required to keep records of such incidents. Also, the 1980 Regulations say that employers should keep records of any inquiries received from the DHSS about claims for industrial injuries benefit relating to 'prescribed' occupational diseases, pneumoconiosis and byssinosis.

It is significant therefore, that the 1983 proposals included a major extension of the NADOR provisions to take in requirements of the notification of chronic occupational ill-health. The consultative document proposed that the existing ill-health requirements in the NADOR (and the Factories Act 1961) should be repealed. In their place it was proposed that there should be an obligation to report certain acute ill-health effects, diseases and medical conditions. These fall into two categories of circumstances:

- when a person has lost consciousness or suffered from any other acute health effect requiring first-aid or immediate medical treatment if it resulted from exposure to a toxic substance, severe radiant heat, electricity or an oxygen deficient atmosphere, or from work in a compressed atmosphere;
- when there is a reason to believe that an employee working under given occupational circumstances has one of a specified number of medical conditions or diseases.

The schedule (Proposals for revised arrangements ......schedule 6) is divided into three parts. Part I details the acute health effects listed above. Part II lists acute and chronic conditions like vibration white finger, dermatitis and oil fulliculitis, reports of which will indicate unsatisfactory workplace conditions whenever they occur. This part is based on, but is not identical to, the DHSS's list of prescribed diseases. The 1st part requires the reporting of the first appearance of certain other diseases, which develop over a very long period. (These include Raynaud's disease and fibrosis of the lung).
Thus, the proposed (1983) arrangements for reporting ill-health are thus far more comprehensive than any that have existed to date. For a brief statement regarding the state of progress of these proposals see [6]. See [7,8,9,10] for very useful general criteria for, and criticisms of, accident reporting systems.

2.2 Statistical Information

The statistics for the year 1982 (and after) are currently in preparation at the Health and Safety Executive (HSE). No definite date has been given for the publication, although a provisional date is 'June 1985. The delays in compilation of the HSE report have been attributed to the alterations in the reporting and notification procedures (ie regulations) and changes in the industrial injuries benefits scheme and the consequent reductions in DHSS figures.

Certain tables of health and safety statistics for 1982 have been forwarded (personal communication) with the proviso that there could very well be alterations to figures per se, or that tables will be re-arranged in terms of format. Where appropriate such information is used in this section to supplement the statistics given.

The statistics are abstracted from the most recent, published accident and disease data [11]. Further information has been drawn from the "Manufacturing and Services 1983 Report" [12], and relevant Health and Safety Commission reports (eg "Health and Safety Commission Report 1983-1984) [13].

The situation in the United Kingdom has been complicated as result of the reporting regulations which came into effect in 1981 [4]. Consequently, there is a break in the statistical series as the figures for 1981 onwards will not be comprable with those for earlier years. Also an annual statistical report was not published for 1981.

Project number SPB/18 (HSC) on the 'Revision of the Notification of Accidents and Dangerous Occurrences 1980' is estimated to reach completion in January 1986. Until this time the NADOR 1980 procedure and practice remains effective - therefore, the statistics will be adversely affected until 1986 in terms of comparability.

At the end of this section several tables (A to G) of relevant data are presented. They are reported in Appendices 1 and 2.

With regard to the statistical tables, the term 'accident' refers to an injury to a person rather than an incident. For example, if an incident causes fatal injuries to one person and non-fatal injuries causing more than three days' absence from work to two others, it will be shown as three accidents, one of which is fatal.

The UK statistics rely upon accident incidence or frequency rates, in addition to accident numbers, as an indication of exposure to risk. The incidence rate is the number of accidents per 100,000 employees at risk (the frequency rate is the number of accidents per 100 million man-hours or per 100,000 man-shifts worked by those at risk).

All tables refer to Great Britain, and to calendar years, unless otherwise specified. The Standard Industrial Classification (SIC) referred to in Table D is the 1968 version of a system of classification of establishments according to industry.

As was pointed out earlier, the confusing situation exists of radical changes in the reporting and notification of accidents and diseases because of modifications to the social security laws relating to industrial injury benefits. (Refer to Appendix 2 for the Health and Safety Statistics summary.)

2.3 Bibliography

4. HEALTH AND SAFETY EXECUTIVE (HSE) "The notification of accidents and dangerous occurrences." (NADOR) Health and Safety series booklet HS(R)5. London: Her Majesty's Stationery Office (HMSO). 1980. pp43.

This is a comprehensive booklet which details the latest reporting and notification procedures. The 1980 Reporting and Notification of Accidents Regulations (NADOR9 are included, as are appendices of relevance. Each part of the 1980 Regulations is described under the following sections: What type of incident should be reported; Who is responsible for reporting; Exemptions; What to do in the event of an accident or dangerous occurrence; To whom do you report; Records. Generally, a helpful booklet which is well written.

5. HEALTH AND SAFETY COMMISSION (HSC) "Proposals for revised arrangements for reporting accidents, ill-health, and dangerous occurrences at work." Consultative document. London: HMSO. 1983. pp24.

Bearing in mind the consultative nature of this document, it appears clear and informative as far as re-arrangement of the 1980 NADOR is concerned. The proposals for changes in reporting and notification are described together with proposed regulations which take up a large part of the document.

6.   OCCUPATIONAL SAFETY & HEALTH, "New arrangements for reporting workplace accidents and ill health.   "Sept. 1985, p2.

A recent statement on the progress regarding the HSCs proposals regarding new arrangements for accident, hazard and ill health reporting.

7.   ADAMS, N.L. and HARTWELL, N.M.   "Accident-reporting systems: a basic problem area in industrial society " J. Occupational Psychology, 50, 1977, 285-298.

An extremely useful examination of industrial accident reporting systems. Existing systems are reviewed in terms of operating and communication problems.   Difficulties of reporting incidence and source variability and quality, of utilisation and of outside biasing factors are discussed. Criteria for improved systems are given.

8.   FANNING, D.   The compilation and use of accident statistics in the British Steel Corporation.   B.S.C. - Sheffield Division Sept. 1977. pp 13.

Despite being an internal report referring to only one industry this gives a very lucid account of some of the problems faced by industrialists in operating such systems.

9. KLETZ, T.A.   "Accident data: the need for a new look at the sort of data that are collected and analysed".   J. of Occup. Accidents, 1, p. 95-105, 1976.

Criticises the amount and manner of data collection in many companies, and proposes a more selective approach concentrating on equipment and human reliability.

10. SHANNON, H.S. and MANNING D.P. "A note on reported accident rates". J. of Occup. Accidents, 2, p. 245-253, 1979.

Discussed the variation in results caused by the method of reporting accident rates.

11. HEALTH AND SAFETY EXECUTIVE (HSE) "Health and Safety Statistics 1980." A publication of the Government Statistical Service. London: HMSO. 1983. pp63.

In order to gain an overall picture of the UK's accident and disease position, this detailed book is essential. 'Health and Safety Statistics 1980' is the latest published statistics in the area, and presents the figures for the UK prior to the implementation of the NADOR (1980). Therefore, it is the last report in the series and describes the trends in the UK for the previous decade wherever possible. The statistics are preceeded by an informative commentary which interprets the tables of data contained within the report.

12. HEALTH AND SAFETY EXECUTIVE (HSE) "Manufacturing and Services Industries 1983 report." London: HMSO. 1984. pp80.

The appendices of this report prove helpful in evaluation of health and safety statistics for this major industrial area, in the face of no comprehensive published statistics for recent years. The report assesses the state-of-the-art in manufacturing and services industries and the work of Her Majesty's Factory Inspectorate.

13. HEALTH AND SAFETY COMMISSION (HSC) "Health and Safety Commission Report 1983-1984." London: HMSO. 1984. pp43.

The HSC annual report, of which this is the most recent, include several sections on the latest work and policy of the HSC. The statistics presented are of great use, due to the lack of breakdown - ie their format is fairly simple by comparison with the Health and Safety Series of the HSE. Otherwise, the HSC report summarises the latest efforts in the field of occuptional health and safety in terms of progress made and current developments.

2.4 Tables

A) <u>FATAL INJURIES TO EMPLOYEES AT WORK 1971-1982</u>

Year	All employees in employment (000s)	Fatal Injuries	Incidence rates (per 10,000 employees)
1971	21,643	864	4.0
1972	21,650	812	3.8
1973	22,182	873	3.9
1974	22,297	786	3.5
1975	22,213	729	3.3
1976	22,048	682	3.1
1977	22,126	614	2.8
1978	22,274	628	2.8
1979	22,639	588	2.6
1980	22,458	562	2.5
1981	21,386	521	2.4
1982	20,825	507	2.4

Source: Health and Safety Executive Statistics personally communicated.

B) <u>DEATHS FROM OCCUPATIONAL DISEASES RESULTING IN AWARDS OF INDUSTRIAL DEATH</u>
<u>BENEFIT etc. BY SCHEME 1978-1982.</u>

	1978	1979	1980	1981	1982
Industrial injuries scheme death benefit awards:					
(i) pneumoconiosis - (including asbestosis)	(P) 589	(P) 609	(P) 588	(P) 539	(P) 552
(ii) other prescribed diseases	(P) 147	(P) 169	(P) 175	(P) 217	(P) 219
Certification that death was due to pneumoconiosis (Workman's compensation scheme)	54	60	66	68	48
Pneumoconiosis, byssinosis + miscellaneous diseases benefit scheme death benefit awards.	81	77	81	50	54
Total all schemes	871	915	910	874	873

(P) = Provisional

Source: DHSS - Department of Health and Social Security

C) DANGEROUS OCCURRENCES REPORTED TO ENFORCEMENT AUTHORITIES BY TYPE, 1982

Code No.	Type of dangerous occurrence (code description)	No. reported
	Dangerous occurrences to be notifiable in relation to any place of work -	
01	Failure, collapse or overturning of lifting machinery...	704
02	Explosion, collapse or bursting of any closed vessel...	277
03	Electrical fault causing fire or explosion...	153
04	Explosion or fire due to ignition of process materials, waste or finished products	340
05	Uncontrolled release or escape of highly flammable liquids.	106
06	Collapse or part collapse of scaffold.	38
07	Collapse or partial collapse at any building or structure under construction.	29
08	Uncontrolled release or escape of potentially harmful substance.	670
09	Personal exposure to, or contact with, a harmful substance, or lack of oxygen.	147
10	Ill-health resulting from exposure to isolated pathogens or infected material.	13
11	Ignition of explosion of explosives	86
12	Failure or collapse of a lifted freight container or part thereof.	10
13	Bursting, explosion or collapse of a pipe-line or any part thereof or the ignition of anything in a pipe-line.	97
14	Overturning or serious damage to the tank while conveying prescribed hazardous substance.	28
	Dangerous occurrences which are notifiable in relation to mines:	
21	Ignition of gas or dust below ground	9
22	Accidental gas ignition on the surface	10
23	Outbreaks of fire below ground	65

Code No.	Type of dangerous occurrence (code description)	No. reported
24	Withdrawal of men owing to smoke	16
25	Fires on the surface	2
26	Outbursts	2
27	Breakage of man-carrying ropes, etc. in shaft staple pits and unwalkable outlets	4
28	Breakage of man-carrying ropes, etc. below ground	19
29	Overwinds	4
30	Breakdown of ventilating apparatus	140
31	Collapse of certain surface buildings or structures	2
32	Failure of breathing apparatus, etc.	-
33	First-aid or medical treatment arising out of use of breathing apparatus, etc.	1
34	Electric shock or burns	20
35	Injuries from blasting materials or devices	9
36	Use of apparatus in pursuance of the Mines (Emergency Egress) Regulations 1973	7
37	Inrushes of gas from old workings	2
38	Inrushes of water, etc.	7
39	Unstable or potentially unstable waste heaps or settling ponds.	1
	Dangerous occurrences which are notifiable in relation to quarries	
51	Collapse of load-bearing structure	3
52	Sinking or overturning of waterborne craft of hovercraft.	-
53	Injuries from blasting materials or devices	3
54	Substance projected beyond quarry boundaries by blasting operations	24
55	Electric shock or burns	6
56	Unstable or potentially unstable tip	12

Code No.	Type of dangerous occurrence (code description)	No. reported
	Dangerous occurrences which are notifiable in relation to railways:	
61	Failure of locomotive	1
62	Failure of railway vehicle	-
63	Failure of rope haulage system	2
64	Failure of permanent way or formation	-
65	Trains or vehicles striking obstruction on line	-
66	Collision, derailment or trains becoming divided	1
67	Failure of level crossing equipment or trains (unauthorised) running onto level crossings	-
68	Other not elsewhere classified	82
	Total:	3152

Source: [13]

D)   INJURIES TO EMPLOYEES, REPORTABLE TO
ENFORCEMENT AUTHORITIES: BY SEVERITY
OF INJURY 1982 (REVISED) AND
BROAD INDUSTRIAL ANALYSIS

Order No.	Standard Industrial Classification (SIC)	Fatal Injuries	Major Injuries	Fatal and Major (no)	Injuri (rates per 100,00
i	Agriculture, forestry, fishing	27	147	174	49.1
ii	Mining and Quarrying	73	1059	1132	349.3
iii	Food, drink, tobacco	10	530	540	89.9
iv	Coal & petroleum products	3	50	53	211.2
v	Chemicals & allied industries	6	332	338	88.0
vi	Metal manufacture	27	470	497	171.4
vii	Mechanical engineering	18	457	475	66.2
viii	Instrument engineering	–	31	31	23.9
ix	Electrical engineering	8	180	188	29.2
x	Shipbuilding and Marine eng.	8	148	156	112.0
xi	Vehicles	5	267	272	49.7
xii	Metal goods not elsewhere specified	10	396	406	96.7
xiii	Textiles	6	198	204	68.5
xiv	Leather, leather goods, fur	–	26	26	91.9
xv	Clothing and footwear	1	35	36	14.0
xvi	Bricks, pottery, glass, cement	11	229	240	118.9
xvii	Timber, furniture, etc.	6	290	296	145.2
xviii	Paper, printing, publishing	6	269	275	56.0
xix	Other manufacturing industries	2	145	147	62.4
	Total all manufacturing industries	127	4053	4180	74.4
xx	Construction	100	1950	2050	204.0
xxi	Gas, electricity, water	13	169	182	55.2
xxii	Transport, communication	52	523	575	42.4
xxiii	Distribution trades	10	219	229	8.6
xxiv	Insurance, banking, finance.	3	9	12	0.9
xxv	Professional and scientific services	4	1103	1107	30.3
xxvi	Miscellaneous services	16	516	532	21.8
xxvii	Public administration and defence	14	1051	1065	71.3
	Unclassified (†)	32	1491	1523	–

Total all injuries   471   12290   12761   62.2

(† = mainly injuries reported to local authorities, approx

400 returns.

Source: [13]

E.) INJURIES TO EMPLOYEES AND OTHERS REPORTED TO HSC/HSE ENFORCEMENT
AUTHORITIES, 1982.
(Summary Table)

Employees		Self-employed and other non-employees	
Fatal injury	Major injury	Fatal injury	Major injury
471	12,290	132	5,749

Source: [13]

(F) REPORTED GASSING ACCIDENTS 1982: ALL FACTORIES ACT
PREMISES (THERE WERE NO FATALITIES)

Ammonia	1
Benzene	-
Toluene, xylene and other homologues of benzene	1
Petroleum distillates (white spirit and coal tar naptha)	1
Other hydrocarbons	2
Carbon dioxide	5
Carbon monoxide	-
Blast furnace gas	-
The oven gas	-
Other	4
Carbon tetrachloride	-
Methylene chloride	1
Perchloroethylene	1
Trichloroethylene	2
Other chlorinated hydrocarbons	-
Non-chlorine halogenated hydrocarbons	4
Chlorine	9
Hydrogen chloride	1
Hydrogen cyanide	-
Hydrogen sulphide	1
Formaldehyde and other aldehydes	-
Isocyanates	3
Metal fumes	1
Nitrous fumes (oxides of nitrogen other than nitrogen oxide)	-
Phosgene	-
Sulphur oxides (sulphur dioxide & sulphur trioxide)	9
Other fumes	23
TOTAL	69

Source: Employment Medical Advisory Service. Health and Safety
        1981-1982 (HSE).

(G) <u>NOTIFIED CASES OF INDUSTRIAL POISONING 1982: ALL FACTORIES
    ACT PREMISES: (THERE WERE NO FATALITIES</u>)

<u>Disease</u>

Disease	
Aniline poisoning	6
Anthrax	-
Arsenical poisoning	-
Beryllium poisoning	1
Cadmium poisoning	1
Carbon bisulphide poisoning	-
Chrome ulceration	18
Chronic benzene poisoning	-
Compressed air illness	-
Epitheliomatous ulceration	-
Lead poisoning	4
Manganese poisoning	-
Phosphorous poisoning	-
Toxic anaemia	-
Toxic jaundice	-
TOTAL	30

Source: Employment Medical Advisory Service. Health and
          Safety 1981-1982 (HSE).

CHAPTER 3

COMPENSATION FOR OCCUPATIONAL INJURIES AND DISEASES

The aim of this chapter is to provide an overall description of the legal basis, and other criteria, for compensation in respect of occupational accidents and diseases for the United Kingdom. Efforts have been made to keep the text clear and intelligible for readers who are not expert in legal terminology. However, it is felt that the following terms do require definition:

'damages' - compensation in money for personal injuries and other loss or damage

'liability' - an obligation to pay damages which can be enforced by an action

'negligence' - failure to take reasonable care when a duty to do so is imposed by law

'subrogation' - the rule whereby a person discharging the liability of another acquires any right of relief or otherwise belonging to that other

'tort' - conduct which gives rise to an action for damages, such as negligence or breach of statutory duty

Contents

3.1 The Industrial Injuries Benefits Scheme
3.2 Other forms of compensation
3.3 Summary and conclusions
3.4 Bibliography

3.1 The Industrial Injuries Benefits Scheme (I.I.B.S.)

The industrial injuries benefits scheme (I.I.B.S.) is designed to provide a comprehensive range of benefits to compensate for the effects of injuries sustained at work and certain diseases contracted as a result of work or working conditions. This form ofcompensation (the state's compensation scheme) is designed not only to make up for earnings lost in the short-or long-term, but also to make amends for temporary or permanent loss of faculty which may occur without affecting actual earning capacity. The I.I.B.S. is part of the national insurance (N.I.) scheme and contributions to the latter are compulsory.

Benefits are not dependent upon proof of fault or negligence, yet causal connection between employment and injury has not been severed from the scheme (in that the injury must arise 'out of' the employment). Payment to the victim or their dependants is generally in the form of periodic payments or a pension as opposed to a lump sum. At present, the state does not exercise subrogation rights through the claimant against 'private' insurance.

The state's involvement in industrial injuries dates to the Workmens Compensation Act 1897. This was the first of a series of statutes imposing liability upon employers, providing the basis upon which the state was able to take over the responsibility (or paying such compensation when the present scheme was established (National Insurance (Industrial Injuries) Acts 1945, 1946). The current statutory provisions are found in the Social Security Act 1975 [14] and a number of amending statutes. The aim of the legislation has been to provide a statute embodying the general principles of the benefit scheme whilst giving the power to make regulations to spell out the detail of statutory provisions.

Another source of law (after statutes and regulations) upon which the I.I.B.S. is dependent is the decisions made by the National Insurance Commissioners on appeal from local tribunals. These have provided for the establishment of a coherent body of case-law on the interpretation of the provisions of statutes and regulations.

Entitlement to the individual benefits in the I.I.B.S. will, of course, depend upon the circumstances of the claimant. However, there are certain basic conditions which must be fulfilled in every claim. Extracting the major conditions from the Social Security Act 1975, s 50 (1)', the claimant must show that as:

    1)   "...an employed earner..."

    2)   "...he/she suffers personal injury caused by accident..."

    3)   "...after 4th 'July, 1948..."

    4)   "...arising out of and in the course of his/her employment".

These criteria will now be considered separately.

1)   "...an employed earner..." Only those who are employed earners are entitled to industrial injuries benefit; the self-employed are excluded from the scheme. An employed earner is defined as "...a person who is gainfully employed in Great Britain either under contract of service, or in an office (including elective office) with emoulments chargeable to income tax under Schedule E."

2)   "...he/she suffers personal injury caused by accident..." To have suffered personal injury the claimant must have suffered hurt to body or mind" (psychological injury is included as well as physical injury). Diseases resulting from accidents are included. The claimant must show, on a balance of probabilities, that the accident "caused" the injury, although it may only be a contributory cause. The word "accident" has presented many difficulties. Whilst deliberate acts of the injured party cannot be accidents, deliberate acts of a third party can be. A process (such as breathing in dust)', which occurs over a long period of time, must be distinguished from an accident: the distinction is a fine one. Where the injury is caused by a process, entitlement under the I.I.B.S. depends on being able to show that the claimant is suffering from one of the prescribed injuries or diseases (refer to appendix 4.

3)   "...after 4th July, 1948..."   If the accident occurred before the 5th 'July, 1948 the claimant will not be covered by the I.I.B.S.

4)   "...arising out of and in the course of his/her employment..."   Basically, this means that the accident must happen at work (not normally travelling to and from work). Not only must the accident happen at work but it must also be linked to the work itself so that it can be said that the work itself led, in some way, to the injury.   The employment must create a risk different to that which would be faced by that employee as a member of the general public.   If work was a material cause, then a prior condition, even if it rendered a person more liable to have an accident, is irrelevant.

If the claimant suffers from one of the prescribed diseases and injuries (see appendix 4) then he/she is entitled to benefit provided:

1)   he/she has been employed in an occupation of the nature prescribed for that disease, and
2)   the disease or injury was caused by that occupation.

The prescribed diseases and injuries include pneumoconiosis (including silicosis and asbestosis)', byssinosis and about fifty other conditions.   Sometimes a prescribed disease in turn causes other diseases (sequalar) which are not prescribed but the resulting sequalae are treated as though they were.

Each listed disease or injury is prescribed for a particular occupation: Claimants will be entitled to benefit only if they can show that they were suffering from the disease or injury and that it was due to the nature of the relevant occupation.

The benefits to which a person is entitled when incapable of work due to an occupational accident or a prescribed injury or disease were modified from 6th April, 1983. Now, claimants are entitled to statutory sick pay from their employers during the first eight weeks of incapacity, at the end of which sickness and invalidity benefits may be payable to those who have made sufficient N.I. contributions, and to those incapable of work due to an occupational (industrial) accident or a prescribed injury or disease.

The reform of the I.I.B.S. (in 1983), generally speaking, does not increase the payments available but redistributes them among claimants, giving more to the severely disabled at the expense of the less severely disabled. The system of benefits has been 'simplified' - for example, injury benefit, death benefit, unemployability supplement, hospital treatment allowance, and constant attendance allowance have been abolished or re-named.

The main benefit under the I.I.B.S. is disablement benefit, and is payable if the claimant is still disabled fifteen weeks after the accident or onset of the disease whether or not he/she is then able to work. Disablement benefit represents compensation for loss of faculty, the disablement itself. Special hardship allowance (re-named reduced earnings allowance) is payable to compensate for loss of earnings and to provide for the needs of the very severely injured.

Note that the relevant legislation for the I.I.B.S. is contained in "The Law Relating to Social Security and Child Benefits" (4 volumes; 1975 and supplements, H.M.S.O.) and "Social Security Case Law, Digest of Commissioner's Decisions" (2 volumes).
(See also [15 and 16]).

3.2   Other Forms of Compensation

If a person is injured as a result of the fault or negligent conduct (tort) of another, they can then receive compensation in respect of such an injury, in a number of ways. The entitlement and receipt of benefit(s) under the I.I.B.S. does not prevent an action for damages (that is, one's right to sue an employer) if negligence or breach of statutory duty can be shown. However, benefits do affect, to a limited extent, the amount of damages recoverable. Compensation through the tort system (employer's liability) is the second major channel of compensation, and effectively dates to nineteenth century case law and the Law Reform (Personal Injuries) Act 1948.

Tort damages are in the form of a lump sum. They are paid by the defendants in civil actions and are normally handled by private liability insurance. Before any damages or insurance moneys can be paid out in respect of liability, fault must be proved; hence, such insurance is often termed liability insurance.

Employer's liability (liability of an employer to pay damages to servants for personal injuries which they sustained in the course of their work) may be incurred in a number of ways [14]. 'Personal liability' refers to an employer liable if an accident is due to the employer's own act or default - for example, dangerous operations conducted without establishing a safe method of work. The employer is also responsible for the acts of servants in the course of their employment - for example, where one worker injures another through carelessness. This is known as 'vicarious' liability. In general, both personal and vicarious liability have, as a result of the 1948 Act, been integrated into a single duty. Liability of this general kind is common law liability (that is, arising out of the ordinary or common law of the land as interpreted by the courts) where proof of negligence is required.

In addition, there is liability for breach of statutory duty (that is, failure to comply with a duty imposed by an Act of Parliament or by regulations) such as the Factories Act 1961 and the Health and Safety at Work etc. (HASAW) Act 1974. This type of liability has the advantage of simplicity: The injured worker does not have to prove negligence, but simply breach of the statute causing an accident.

The HASAW Act generalised the safety legislation and imposed safety obligations on all employers. Now, the administration of the safety laws is centralised in a single authority and will be simplified. Eventually, new codes of regulations under the 1974 Act will replace the various special Acts. Meanwhile, they remain in force within the framework of the Act. One innovation of the 1974 Act is that it creates duties towards outsiders who are affected by industrial accidents.

A third source of compensation (after the I.I.B.S. and common law compensation) stems from the Criminal Injuries Compensation Scheme 1964. Here, compensation consists of ex gratia payments and is confined to situations where injury arises through the commission of a criminal offence upon a person.

Finally, there is compensation payable in respect of an injury insured under a personal accident policy. This sort of insurance is voluntary and mostly used by the self-employed.

3.3 Summary and conclusions

Having briefly described the two major forms of compensation in the U.K. (the Industrial Injuries Scheme, and the tort system), it now makes sense to report recent comments and criticisms of the situation as a whole with respect to this country's plethora of systems. Also, the Pearson Commission's Report and findings (the most recent survey of civil liability and personal injury) requires further note [18, 19].

Hard on the heels of the proposals for reforming the law relating to prescribed industrial diseases followed the report containing proposals for the I.I.B.S. reform. Both White Papers came after certain recommendations in the Report of the Pearson Commission. It should be noted that legislative changes based upon these proposals took effect in 1984.

As was mentioned earlier, the present situation in the U.K. involves mixed systems (tort compensation, I.I.B.S., liability insurance, etc.) which have now existed alongside each other for many years. Of course, this has sometimes led to patial double indemnity in that injured workers were compensated to some extent under both public and private systems. The Pearson report advocated, effectively, that the state's social security system be the major vehicle for compensating work injuries.

The tort system of compensation, where claimants have to prove fault (that is, negligence) in order to obtain redress for injuriessuffered at work, has been criticised for a number of years. It is true that justice and access to compensation is beyond the reach of many of those who may be (as a result of work) seriously in need under the tort system. Justice, it seems, is only available to those poor enough to qualify for legal aid, or alternatively, those affluent enough to do without it. Another problem with this system of compensation is the delay factor, some cases taking five or six years to settle in court. The costly cases involving civil liability take too long to come to court. The other main criticism of the tort system of compensation is the fact that claimants (litigants) are expected to remember in detail, with ease and clarity, the circumstances surrounding the accident which may have occurred years before.

The Pearson Commission and subsequent reports have cited examples of better (that is, more integrated or comprehensive) systems, and looked at those belonging to the U.S.A., Sweden, Canada, Australia and in particular New Zealand. It is highly unlikely that any radical reforms or developments will occur as a result of such investigation, bearing in mind the complex existing legal framework. The Pearson report did suggest, however, that tort be subordinated, as a compensation vehicle, to state social security and some progress has been made in this respect.

The shortcomings of the common law's mechanisms for providing compensation for occupational accidents have been debated. However, considerably less consideration has been given to the equally distressing plight of those who suffer from a gradual deterioration in health as a result of long term exposure to hazardous working conditions, and to the special difficulties which may be encountered in the use of the law of negligence to obtain some redress for this type of disablement. It is ironic that these people may have a particular need for common law damages because they have no claim under the I.I.B.S. (In other words, claimants who suffer from occupational ill-health and disease not covered by the current 'prescribed diseases'). The Pearson report estimated that only about 10.5 per cent of all those injured at work receive tort compensation, and the percentage of employees who are compensated for 'ill-health' may well be lower than this figure. It has been suggested that the ultimate solution to the problem of providing for those who suffer a disabling deterioration in health might be an improved state system able to cover adequately all forms of disability however caused. (In view of the present UK Government's erosion of the 'welfare state' and the social security system, such a solution may appear rather optimistic).

Recently, some employers have been introducing their owncompensation schemes for employees suffering from certain occupational diseases [20]. Essentially, this provides an alternative for the employee who might otherwise have resorted to a costly, long civil action, since when the employee gets to enter such a scheme he/she must give up his/her rights to claim damages. On the employer's side, the introduction of such a scheme usually makes for better industrial relations since most employees recognise this as a positive step in the right direction.

With respect to reforms in the field of compensation for occupational accidents and diseases, the Pearson report has, in the opinion of many, proved a great disappointment [19, 21]. It is contended that far-reaching reforms might have been devised to dove-tail into the existing legal structure. Perhaps the simplest reform would have been to extend the I.I.B.S. to cover all accidents. Many believe that although there are a great many detailed recommendations in the report, there is a marked lack of overall principle or underlying strategy. For example, the Commission could have provided leadership on the abolition (whole or in part) of the right of action in tort.

What above all else needs reform is the unfairness produced by the lack of integration of the various compensation systems in the U.K. [22, 23, 24, 25]. There is the difficulty of justifying payments under one system but refused by another. There is the difficulty of justifying the different treatments accorded by the law to the victims of disease, and the victims of accidents (and among the latter between victims of fault and no-fault caused accidents). What is surely needs is a comprehensive system based on the existing state system, but with benefits as adequate as society can afford.

3.4 BIBLIOGRAPHY

14 DEPARTMENT OF HEALTH AND SOCIAL SECURITY (D.H.S.S.) "Social Security Act 1975 - Reform of the Industrial Injuries Scheme" Cmnd P042. London: H.M.S.O. November 1981. 30 pp.

The Government's proposals for modernising the thirty three year old benefit scheme are set out in this White Paper. A concise document which puts forward recommendations for the 'simplification' of social security schemes in relation to industrial accidents and diseases and the associated benefits.

15   ROWLAND, M. "The Industrial Injuries Benefits Scheme." Law and practice guide no. 6.   London: Legal Action Group (LAG).   July 1983.   122 pp.

This book is a practical (and recent) guide to the range of state benefits available to people injured at work.   Chapters deal with individual benefits payable to victims of industrial accidents and diseases, entitlement to benefit, as well as coverage of administration and claim procedures.   It is well-written in that the author avoids detailed history of the legislation, and the all-too-common jargon of legal texts.

16   DEPARTMENT OF HEALTH AND SOCIAL SECURITY (D.H.S.S.) "Injured at work, a guide to cash benefits."   (FB. 15/Nov 84);   "Disablement benefit and increases" (NI.196/April 83); "Social security rates and earnings rules" (NI.196/Nov 84); "Industrial death benefits - for widows and other dependants" (N1.10/Mar 83);   "Prescribed industrial diseases (Nl. 2/Dec 84).   London: H.M.S.O.

A set of leaflets, simply written, outlining law and the state benefits in respect of industrial injuries.

17   MUNKMAN, J. "Employers Liability at Common Law."   Ninth edition. London: Butterworths.   1979.   653 pp.

Munkman manages to cover all the major aspects, from a traditional perspective, of liability for accidents at work. Liability and negligence are explained and then shown as they relate to different Acts and corresponding industries.   The law is stated as at 31st December 1978.

18. ROYAL COMMISSION ON CIVIL LIABILITY AND COMPENSATION FOR PERSONAL INJURY. Chairman: Lord Pearson. Volumes 1-3. Cmnd 7054. London: H.M.S.O. 1978.

This report is in three volumes: I - Report (including the recommendations); II - Statistics (costings and survey results); III - Overseas methods of compensation. Generally known as the Pearson Commission report, this constitutes competent review of compensation systems, payments, etc. Although criticised with respect to its recommendations, it remains a valuable and informed piece of research in the area.

19. COLLINSON, J.M. (1979) The Pearson report - compromise or step towards effective and just compensation for disability? British J. of Indust. Med. 36, 263-275.

This article discusses in detail the establishment and goals of the Pearson Committee. The main recommendations of the committee are assessed, as are the proposals for reforms in compensation. The author comments "the report itself is a bundle of compromises but one can have sympathy with why this should be so."

20. SOCRATES, E. (1981) "Employer's Compensation Schemes". Occupational safety and health, March 26-27.

Socrates looks at the alternative of employers' compensation schemes which are a recent introduction to the compensation issue. Such schemes relate to occupational diseases primarily, and represent a useful alternative to seeking compensation through the courts.

21. WHINCUP, M.   "Compensation for accidents".   Occ. Health, May, 205-211, 1978. pp 7.

Discusses how the Pearson Commission failed to deal with many important anomalies which exist in the compensation of victims of accidental injury.

22. ATIYAH, P.S. "Accidents, Compensation and the Law." Third edition.   London: Weidenfeld and Nicolson. 1980.   695 pp.

'Accidents, Compensation and the Law' represents a comprehensive and critical survey of the law relating to compensation, such as the social and political aspects. Inconsistencies and anomalies are brought into the open, and the author canvasses possibilities for change.   This edition also takes account of the Pearson Commission findings.

23. BARRET, B. (1981) "Employers' liability for work related ill-health".   Indust. Law J. Vol 10, 101-112.

Barret points out the unfair situation which arises when employees suffer from a gradual deterioration of health as a result of long-term exposure.   Special difficulties may be encountered when employing the law of negligence in the courts.   Barret concludes: "The ultimate solution to the problem...might well be an improved social security system able to cover adequately all forms of disability."

24. WHINCUP, M. (1980) "Compensation for negligence". Occupational Health, April 1980. p.175-183.

Whincup makes a number of points about the methods of negligence compensation in the U.K.   He criticises the system as it stands, and draws upon the New Zealand experiences in support of his argument.   The article refers to several examples from case law which emphasise the anxieties of seeking compensation through the courts.

25. WILSON, S.R.   "Occupational Diseases;   the problems of a comprehensive system of coverage."   Industrial Law Journal, volume II, 141-155, 1982.

This is a critical appraisal of the British Industrial Injuries Scheme which is based upon a listing of prescribed diseases.   The author makes comparisons with the American coverage of occupational diseases, and concludes with comments about injustice vis-a-vis non-prescribed work-related diseases.

CHAPTER 4

INFORMATION AVAILABLE ON FOUR SPECIFIC HAZARDS/ACCIDENT TYPES

Contents:

4.1 Fatal accidents
  1 Reporting and notifying criteria
  2 Relevant general and specific legislation
  3 Statistics
  4 Compensation criteria

4.2 Falls from heights
  1 Reporting and notifying criteria
  2 Relevant general and specific legislation
  3 Statistics
  4 Compensation criteria
  5 Prevention measures

4.3 Noise - occupational deafness
  1 Reporting and notifying criteria
  2 Relevant general and specific legislation
  3 Statistics
  4 Compensation criteria
  5 Inspection agencies and criteria
  6 Prevention measures
  7 Records

4.4 Asbestos
  1 Reporting and notification criteria
  2 Relevant general and specific legislation
  3 Statistics
  4 Compensation criteria
  5 Inspection procedures
  6 Prevention measures

4.5 Bibliography

This chapter attempts to compile the available information on the four specific hazard/accident types listed above. The literature searched is primarily that of state agencies and government publications.

4.1 Fatal accidents

4.1.2. Reporting and notifying criteria   One of the three categories for the purposes of notification of accidents which arise out of or in connection with work [4] is fatal accidents. They have to be reported whether the person who dies is employed or not, and the reporting must be to the HSE (enforcing authority).   For example, a member of the public falling into a hole on a construction site would be a directly reportable accident.

There is a further duty, due to the NADOR, to provide a repo written t of an accident which became fatal within one of t year of the date e accident, although it had previously non- been reported as atal.

4.1.2 Relevant and specific legislation

The prevention of fatal accident or accidents in general is an integral part of the Health and Safety at Work Act 1974 (HASAWA).   The specific legislation relating to 'fatal accidents' is mainly that pertaining to notification and reporting (see above).

4.1.3 Statistics

The reader is requested to refer to Tables A, B, D and E in Section 2 which presents a series of UK statistics including the figures for fatal accidents. Falls from heights resulting in a fatality are dealt with in the next section (4.2.3.).

4.1.4 Compensation criteria

The Department of Health and Social Security (DHSS) offer guidance on the issue of compensation for fatal accidents arising out of or in connection with work in the leaflet "Industrial Death Benefit - for widows and other dependants" [26]. This benefit falls under the industrial injuries benefit scheme which is state-run.

Death benefits are payable to widows and dependent children and, in certain circumstances, to widowers, other relatives and women having care of a child of the deceased where a person has died as a result of:
- an accident at work; or
- a prescribed industrial disease.
By comparison with other benefits in the IIBS, the eligibility and claiming of industrial death benefit is complex.

The nature of this benefit and the way in which it operates may be seen to discriminate in terms of sex of worker. The 'widow' as opposed to remaining spouse or dependants, appears to be anachronistic and, therefore, due for revision.

Leaflet NI 10 [26] details the criteria for compensation in respect of fatal occupational accidents. Claims for benefit must be made to the DHSS on form BW1. However, re-organisation of the IIBS in 1983/4 meant that death benefit of those killed at work was abolished. Existing claimants are still protected under the 'old' death benefit rules.

The HSE produce a number of reports of various types of industrial accident fatalities (e.g. [27]). Additional sources are rare due to the infrequent nature of such accidents and the absence of the chief witness!

4.2 Falls from Heights

4.2.1 Reporting and notification criteria

Under the NADOR [4] falls from heights are notifiable to the HSE where they result in fatal or major injury accidents. The definition of 'major injury' covers the following:
- fracture of the skull, spine, or pelvis;
- fracture of any bone

i) in the arm, other than a bone in the wrist or hand;

ii) in the leg, other than a bone in the ankle or foot;
- any other injury which results in the person injured being admitted into hospital for more than twenty-four hours as an in-patient, unless the person is only detained for observation. The above categories of injury are those in the major injury class which are most commonly associated with falls from heights. As such they must be directly reported.

However, the above ignore 'other accidents' which are not directly reportable to the HSE. Other accidents, known for many years as "three day accidents" in factories or construction sites were, prior to the NADOR, reported to Her Majesty's Factory Inspectorate on Form 43 or 43B.

Falls from heights may also be included under the dangerous occurrences schedule of the NADOR. For the purposes of reporting this type of incident it does not matter whether or not injury results - the aim is to obtain information about incidents which have the potential for death or major injury. Reporting (direct) is to the HSE on form F2508.

The following dangerous occurrences (from Regulation 3(2)) might relate to falls from heights...
"- collapse or overturning of any lift, hoist, crane, excavator, or mobile powered access platform or failure of any load-bearing part thereof which, taking into account the circumstances of the occurrence, might have been liable to cause a major injury to any person..."

"- a collapse or part collapse of any scaffold which is more than twelve metres high which results in a substantial part of the scaffold falling or overturning."

4.2.2 General and specific relevant legislation

Many maintenance and cleaning jobs, in particular, involve work at a height, for example roof repairs, lift maintenance, servicing of heating or air conditioning, house painting and window cleaning.

For all these purposes the duty of the Health and Safety at Work Act 1974 (HASAWA) S2 requires every employer to take such steps as are necessary to prevent a fall.

Additionally, every occupier of premises has a duty under the Occupiers Liability Act 1957 to take such care as in all the circumstances is reasonable to see that a visitor to the premises is safe. This general duty and the HASAWA provision reinforce each other.

There are certain specific provisions relevant to falls from heights, for example S29 of the Factories Act 1961. There are many provisions in regulations made under this Act which regulate works of construction, building operations and engineering works where potential hazards arising from work on temporary structures, scaffolding, falsework, etc. are present. Under the Factories Act 1961, if the place at which any person has to work is a place from which he/she will be liable to fall a distance of 1.98 metres, the place must be provided, as far as is reasonably practicable, with fencing, or other means to ensure an employee's safety (unless there are secure footholds and handholds). This applies to every workplace - ie it covers not only all permanent parts of the premises but will include temporary scaffolding or staging which may be used as a place of work or to reach a place of work.

As far as the construction industry is concerned, the following specific provisions are applicable, unless otherwise specified. The provisions emanate from the Construction (Working Places) Regulations 1966.

(i) Sloping roofs

A sloping roof is a roof or part of a roof having a pitch of more than ten degrees. Where the sloping roof is a means of access or egress, sufficient and suitable crawling ladders, or crawling boards, must be provided on the sloping roof, unless battens or similar members of the roof structure provide adequate foothold and handhold. Except where the work is not extensive or the fall from the eaves of the roof is not more than 1.98 metres, either

- the work must be done from a securely supported working platform not less than 431.8mm wide; or
- a barrier must be provided at the lower edge of the sloping roof which is of such design and construction as to prevent any person falling from the edge.

(ii) Fragile roofs

No person must pass across or work on or from material which would be liable to fracture if the person's weight were applied to it and the fall would be greater than 1.98 metres. Where any person passes on or near or works on or near fragile materials, warning notices must be affixed at approaches to the place, except where the material consists wholly of glass.

To prevent a person passing over or working on fragile material from falling through it, the following provisions, as necessary, must be made:

- suitable guardrails;
- suitable coverings; and
- any other suitable means.

Other specific provisions and regulations apply to safety nets and safety belts (eg Reg 38)(1)), work on temporary structures (Reg 50(1))', the provision of guardrails, etc. (Reg 28(1)), and lifting appliances (Reg 17) - under the Construction (General Provisions) Regulations 1966.

4.2.3 Statistics

From the HSE's (1981) "Fatal accidents in Construction 1978"[27], the proportion of all such accidents which involved falls was 55% (66 out of 120) compared to 45% in the preceding five years. The figures with respect to height of fall were:

HEIGHT OF FALL (1978)	Number
Less than 3m	6
3m to 6m	11
6m to 9m	16
9m and more	33
Total	66

It is reported that a high proportion of these 66 accidents (23%) happened to those working on fragile roofs.

The HSE (1983) report "Construction. Health and Safety 1981-82" [28] provides more recent statistics.

DISTRIBUTION OF FATAL ACCIDENTS 1980- 81	
Falls of persons	53%
Falling objects	16
Transport	14
Electricity	5
Machinery	6
Fire and explosion	1
Not otherwise specified	5

As was noted earlier (Chapter 2) in the discussion of Uk statistics about health and safety, the 1982 data have not yet been published (provisional publication date: June 1985). So, for the same reasons as stated in Chapter 2, "Health and Safety Statistics 1980" [11] was used as the latest published (ie not subject to alteration or re-arrangement) data. From the 1980 statistics the following tables have been extracted:

'ACCIDENTS IN MANUFACTURING INDUSTRIES REPORTED TO HM FACTORY INSPECTORATE, 1980, BY TYPE:

Falls of persons to lower level of 1.98m or less	7,523
Falls of persons to lower level of over 1.98m	1,176
Fall, trip or slip of person on same level	20,538

Source: Table 3.4 p16

ACCIDENTS IN THE CONSTRUCTION INDUSTRY REPORTED TO HM FACTORY INSPECTORATE BY TYPE, 1980

Falls of persons to lower level of 1.98m or less	3,339
Falls of persons to lower level of over 1.98m	1,633
Fall, trip or slip of person on same level	4,270

Source: Table 3.5, p18

4.2.4 Compensation Criteria

Chapter 3 outlined the State benefits for occupational accidents, and falls from heights can be considered in the same light. The DHSS leaflet FB.15 "Injured at Work," (see Chapter 3) describes the benefits available (which were stated previously) for those disabled as a result of an accident at work. Thus, the same criteria for eligibility to the IIBS (and therefore state compensation) apply.

In the case of compensation through damages, there are very few cases brought against employers. Those that reach the courts can be best described as actions for negligence and breach of statutory duty (under The Factories Act 1961, and the Construction (General Provisions) Regulations 1966).

4.2.5 Prevention Measures

The main prevention measures with regard to falls from heights are via the specific legislation. To illustrate, Reg 35(8) of the Construction (Working Provisions) Regulations deals with crawling ladders and boards. The requirement is that they be:
- of good construction, suitable and sound material, adequate strength, free from patent defect and properly maintained;
- properly supported; and
- securely fixed or anchored to the sloping surface or over the roof ridge; or otherwise securely fixed so as to prevent slipping.

Manning has published a number of papers concerning the epidemiology and prevention of falls [29]. The HSE has provided several guidance leaflets for those liable to suffer falls from heights (e.g. [30], [31]).

The underlying principle is that if it is not possible to work safely from the ground or other part of a building or structure, suitable access equipment or other safeguards must be provided. In fact, most large employers will incude such aspects as part of their accident prevention programmes and in their contract documents, etc. Much of the literature concerning falls from heights is encompassed within moves for safety in construction (eg the 'Site Safe '83 campaign').

4.3 NOISE AND OCCUPATIONAL DEAFNESS

4.3.1 Reporting and notifying criteria

The reporting and notifying criteria relating to noise and occupational deafness are as stated earlier in sections 2 and 3. The criteria pertaining to noise levels are outlined in 4.3.2. below.

4.3.2 Relevant general or specific legislation

It was thought that once the HASAWA had been passed one of the first codes of practice to be made would be on noise: however, this has not happened. The only code currently applicable is the Department of Employment (D.E.) voluntary code of 1972 [32]. Noise levels are specifically controlled, at the moment, in only three work situations:

    (a) use of woodworking machines in factories

    (b) tractor cabs

    (c) offshore operations

Otherwise control is maintained by the provisions of the Factories Act 1961 and the HASAWA 1974.

A consultative document ('Protection of Hearing at Work') was issued by the H.S.C. in 1981 [33]. This included draft regulations, to be supported by a Code of Practice, containing provisions which would apply to all places of work.

Occupational deafness is a prescribed industrial disease, for which disablement benefit is payable. Damages may also be awarded against the employer.

The HASAWA doesn't refer to noise specifically but it is clearly applicable to noise. It allows for supplementary regulations to be made for almost all matters covered by the Act.

Similarly, there is no specific reference to noise in the Factories Act 1961, although it is provided that every place of work must, so far as is reasonably practicable, be made and kept safe for any working person therein. This provision is wide enough to provide protection against noise.

The only regulation dealing specifically with noise in factories has been the Woodworking Machines Regulations (1974), Reg.44. It applies to those employed in a 'factory' (as defined by the Factories Act 1961) who are at risk because of exposure to noise of woodworking machinery.

The following requirements are laid down:

a. Where a person is likely to be exposed on any day for eight hours to an equivalent continuous sound level of 90 dB(A) or above, all reasonably practicable measures shall be taken to reduce all noise to the largest extent reasonably practicable; and

b. suitable personal hearing protection shall be provided and maintained and used by persons at risk.

(It should be noted that the exposure to noise is determined as in [32].

With respect to offshore installations there are two applicable regulations - Offshore Installations (Construction and Survey) Regulations 1974, and Offshore Installations (Operational Safety, Health and Welfare) Regulations 1976 - which require:

a. the suitable insulation of every item of equipment capable of causing noise or vibration which is:
- injurious to health, or
- likely to be injurious to health.

b. the provision of suitable protective equipment (including ear protection) for all persons engaged in operation where they are exposed to risk of injury or disease.

The Agriculture (Tractor Cabs) Regulations 1974 also deals with noise, in that noise levels in tractor cabs must not exceed 90dBA.

The voluntary Code of Practice (mentioned earlier) continues to provide guidance and recommended limits to noise exposure as well as describing methods of measurement, and advising on measures to be taken by both management and employees in the general reduction of noise and sound levels. The Code has received widely spread recognition and is considered the definitive U.K. noise standard to which industry works. It also forms the basis for the proposed Protection of Hearing Regulations. The Code is not a legal instrument but a voluntary code to protect the hearing of people at work.

The Code of Practice applies to all persons employed in industry who are exposed to noise. It sets out recommended limits to noise exposure, and methods of measurement to determine whether the limits are exceeded. In addition, some advice is given with the aim of reducing noise levels. The essential detail of the Code concerns the noise limit of an equivalent continuous sound level of 90dB(A) for a period of 8 hours. Higher levels are permitted for shorter periods (for example, 99dB(A) for one hour, 96dB(A) for two hours, 93dB(A) for four hours). However, the Code doesn't place specific limits on the emission of noise from industrial machines.

In the proposed regulations and code of practice ("Protection of Hearing at Work", 1981, [33]), which remain in draft form, all places of work are covered. The general provisions were based on the voluntary Code. It is proposed that employers are to be under a general duty, so far as is reasonably practicable, to ensure that exposure to noise likely to be injurious to hearing is reduced to the lowest level, irrespective of ear protectors provided and worn. In other words, even if an employer succeeds in maintaining a noise level under 90dB(A) Leq (8hr) or 600 Pa, he must keep noise at a level where it is not likely to be injurious to hearing. Here he/she can employ any suitable method to fulfill the obligation.

Protectors or reduced time exposed to noise may only be used when reasonably practicable methods have failed, it seems.

Also, employers will be under an absolute duty to ensure that no person is exposed to noise levels above 90dB(A) Leq (8hr) or a peak sound pressure of 600 Pa. If an employee's exposure is likely to exceed 90dB(A) Leq (8hr) then employers must arrange for surveys, carried out by qualified personnel, to be made in order to assess both exposure (regardless of ear protectors) and the efficiency of measures taken to reduce exposure. The records kept must be available to employees and/or safety representatives.

Where employees are likely to be exposed to very high noise levels (i.e. above 105 dB(A) Leq (8hr) employers will be under duty to arrange for:

a. audiometric testing of employees likely to be exposed to this limit; and
b. individual monitoring of exposure to employees.

Employers owe the same duties to non-employees as they owe to their own employees, as far as is reasonably practicable, where:

a. such persons are likely to be affected by noise likely to be injurious to hearing; and
b. such noise is due to a cause under the employer's control.

This same document proposes that employees must :-
a. make full and proper use of any control measures; and employees must report any defect in the noise control equipment or ear protectors or operational procedures, to his/her employer without unreasonable delay.
b. co-operate with the employer in carrying out the employee's duties, particularly with regard to individual monitoring of exposure to noise, and in measures necessary for controlling exposure levels.

Again, under the proposed regulations and code of practice every designer, manufacturer, importer and supplier of any article in use at work, must, so far as is reasonably practicable, as a general requirement:

a. ensure that the article, when properly used, doesn't produce noise likely to be injurious to hearing.

b. specifically in relation to exposure above 90dB(A) Leq (8hr) or 600 Pa, provide adequate information with respect to the article, if it is likely to cause exposure of any employee to exceed these limits (irrespective of ear protectors), even though the article is being used properly. Such information should give:

i) the noise likely to be produced during use; and

ii) any measures necessary to minimize resulting exposure to noise.

Moreover, designers, manufacturers, importers and suppliers are to carry out testing examination and research in order to comply with the above.

In addition to, the proposed regulations, the consultative document contains a draft code of practice giving guidance on how to comply with the regulations and draft guidance notes explaining the technology and terminology of noise control.

In 1984 the U.K. responded to the European Commissions (EC) amended directive on noise [34]. The HSC (1981) [39] proposed that hearing tests should be mandatory at levels of exposure above 105dB(A) whereas the amended EC proposal includes an 85dB(A) threshold. Such a heavy reliance on audiometry as part of the range of hearing protection measures as would be required by the EC directive is in conflict with the view of the Confederation of British Industry (CBI) that audiometry should have a minor role. UK Trade Unions, in general, have also opposed mandatory audiometry.

In the amended EC proposal on noise the <u>maximum daily noise exposure limit</u> is 90dB(A) Leq (8hr) and the threshold for obligatory provision of ear protectors and of audiometry tests is 85dB(A). With respect to hearing protectors, under the amended proposal they would have to be supplied at the 85dB(A) noise exposure level but their use would not be mandatory until prevailing noise levels were in excess of 90dB(A). These matters are currently being discussed by such bodies as the CBI, TUC and HSC. See [35] for a critique of current UK standards.

4.3.3 Statistics

The (HSE) (1981) [33] gave the following figures (<u>estimates</u>) in relation to manufacturing industry (excluding office workers).

- 50% (approximately) of workers are exposed to 80dB(A);
- 10% are exposed to 90dB(A);
- less than 2% are exposed to 100dB(A).

From "Health and Safety Statistics 1980" [11] Table 10.2 (Prescribed industrial diseases other than pneumoconiosis and byssinosis cases qualifying for industrial injury or disablement benefit, by disease', DHSS statistical years 1975/6 - 1979/80)

No.	Disease	All cases including awards of disablement benefit not following injury benefit				
48	OCCUPATIONAL DEAFNESS* (Now A10)	1975/6	1976/7	1977/8	1978/9	1979/80
		1533	726	527	555	661

* These figures based on DHSS Medical Board records.

ALL PRESCRIBED	1975/6	1976/7	1977/8	1978/9	1979/80
DISEASES	14726	13799	13198	11874	10214
(excluding those for which no information is available.)					

4.3.4 Compensation Criteria

With respect to state disablement benefit, since February 1975 occupational deafness has been included among the "prescribed industrial diseases" (See Chapter 3 - compensation criteria for occupational accidents and diseases) for which state (i.e. Social Security) disablement benefit is payable. The benefit is payable when the deafness arises from any occupation involving [36]:

a.   the use or supervision or assistance in the use, of pneumatic or percussive tools, or the use of high speed grinding tools, in the cleaning, dressing or finishing of cast metal or ingots, billets or blooms; or

b.   the use, or supervision or assistance in the use of pneumatic or percussive tools on metal in the ship building or ship repairing industries; or

c.   the use, or supervision or assistance in the use, of pneumatic or percussive tools on metals, or for drilling rock in quarries or underground, or in coal mining, for at least an average of one hour per working day; or

d.   work wholly or mainly in the immediate vicinity of, drop-forging plant (including plant for drop stamping or drop hammering) or forging press plant engaged in the shaping of hot metal; or

e.   work wholly or mainly in rooms or sheds where there are machines engaged in weaving man-made or natural (including mineral) fibres, or in the bulking up of fibres in textile manufacturing; or

f.   the use of machines which cut, shape or clean metal nails; or

g.   the use of plasma spray guns for the depositing of metal.

'Any occupation' refers to activities in which an employee engages under his/her contract of employment. The fact that the workforce employed in the business is designated, classified or graded by reference to function, training or skills (e.g. labourer, hot examiner, salvage and forge examiner) does not itself justify a conclusion that each separate designator, classification or grading involves a separate occupation. 'Assistance in the use' of tools qualifies the actual use of the tools not the process in the course of which tools are employed, for a person to be entitled to disablement benefit for occupational deafness, the following conditions must be satisfied:

a. he/she must have been employed at any time on or after 5 July 1948 and for a period or periods (whether before or after 5 July 1948) amounting to not less than twenty years (in the aggregate); and

b. there must be permanent sensorineural hearing loss, and the loss in each ear must be at least 50dB; and

c. a loss of 50dB in one ear, at any rate, must be attributable to noise at work.

In October 1983 several changes were made concerning the rules of eligibility for benefit for occupational deafness. Previous claims that had failed may now be eligible. From 3rd October 1983 the following took effect:

- minimum period worked in the listed jobs (see earlier) was shortened from 20 to 10 years;
- the period within which a claim must be made after being employed in a listed occupation was increased from 12 months to 5 years;
- two jobs were added to the list.

Claims for disablement benefit are now made on form Bl 100(0), and the up-to-date benefit rates of social security benefits can be found in form Nl 196 (See [37], [38], [39]).

A hearing loss must satisfy a number of audiological and clinical criteria before a diagnosis of noise-induced hearing loss can be made with sufficient confidence for medical legal purposes.

Firstly, the hearing loss must be sensorineural in origin and it is necessary for air and bone-conduction audiometric results to be in agreement within experimental limits. Secondly, the audiogram must have the right shape with the classical dip or maximum loss at about 4 kHz, although personal variations do occur and maxima at 3 kHz or 6 kHz are not uncommon. However, a loss of hearing at 4 kHz is not an abolsute diagnostic indication of noise damage. Thirdly, tinnitus (or noises in the ears) may be present immediately following noise exposure and may become permanent. Fourthly, there must have been cause: that is sufficient noise exposure. Correlation of hearing loss with noise emission using the National Physical Laboratory (N.P.L.) data, together with a reasonable statistical probability should be demonstrated before a conclusive diagnosis is made. Finally, there must be no other competing diagnostic possibilities.

Damages can also be awarded against employers. As from 1963, employers have been under notice of the dangers to the hearing of their employees. In the past, damages for deafness have not been high, and many such cases have been settled out of court. In Bailey vs. I.C.I. Ltd. the plaintiff's hearing loss was assessed between 15 and 18 dB. Bailey was awarded £7,000 for the loss of past and future amenity. An employer may have to pay damages for the whole of the hearing loss suffered by an employee even when this is partly the result of prior employment (Heslop vs. Metalblock (Britain) Ltd., 1981). In this case, the plaintiff was awarded damages against his employer for the full extent of hearing loss, amounting to twenty four years, even though for sixteen years he had worked in noisy occupations for other employers. The amount awarded was £7,750.

4.3.5 Inspection agencies and criteria

The various measures of inspection and surveying are detailed in the 1972 DE voluntary Code [32].   It says that all machines and areas where the sound level is above, or marginally below, the limit set out in Section 4 of the Code should be regularly inspected by a competent person for efficiency of the means for noise control.   It is also desirable that all new machines be inspected after installation.

Generally speaking, the Factories Inspectorate and Mines and Quarries Inspectorate of the HSE are responsible for the inspection and monitoring of noisy workplaces.   In order to carry out its duty of enforcing the general duties under the HASAWA and other relevant legislation, the HSE is empowered to appoint inspectors (known as HSE inspectors).

An inspector may serve an improvement notice if he is of the opinion that 'a person' -

a. is contravening one or more of the 'relevant statutory provisions';

b. has contravened one or more of those provisions in circumstances that make it likely that the contravention will continue to be repeated.

The period specified in the notice within which the requirement must be carried out must not be less than twenty one days - thus being the period within which an appeal may be lodged with an industrial tribunal.

If an inspector is of the opinion that, with regard to which Sec 22 (1) (HASAWA) applies, the activities involve or will involve, a risk of serious personal injury, he/she may serve on that person a prohibition notice.   Prohibition notices differ from improvement notices in two important ways:

a. with prohibition notices, it is necessary that an
    inspector believes that a provision of the HASAWA or any
    other statutory provision is being or has been
    contravened;
b. prohibition notices are served in anticipation of danger.

In the U.K. an HSE inspector would have cause for concern
if the Code of Practice is not followed, or that an employer
does not attempt to comply with the guidance therein.

4.3.6 Prevention measures

Again, the U.K. position with respect to noise prevention
measures is contained within the Code [32]. The
recommendations are summarized below:

General

-   The best practical means for noise reduction should be
    applied;
-   Design and construction of noise control measures should
    be supervised by a skilled person;
-   Measurements should be made by A-weighted sound level
    meter(s) (i.e. in dB(A)) with supplemental noise
    frequency analysis whenever appropriate.

A Health and Safety Executive (HSE) guide [40]
illustrates specific measures for reducing noise in the
industrial workplace.
Some commonly adopted noise control methods are outlined below
(summarised from [32]:

- Separation of noisy areas.
Where practicable machines producing sound levels in excess of
Code limits should be set apart. Suitable partitions (of
correct size and location with regard to noise sources) may be
needed to prevent noise spread.

Separation of quiet and noisy areas should be as complete as possible: this may be achieved by extending partitions to walls and ceilings (or roof) ensuring minimum openings in the partition. It may be necessary to provide sound-absorbing material in noisy areas to prevent an increase of sound level due to reflection.

- Exhaust silencing

Exhaust systems should be provided with effective silencers, or should be discharged in an area remote from employees. Silencers should be regularly inspected and maintained.

- Machine enclosure

Noisy machines should be provided with sound-insulating enclosures where practicable, and the operator(s) should remain outside the enclosure.

- Enclosure of operator workplace

It may be possible to protect the operator by providing a sound-reducing enclosure or cabin, in which case attention should be paid to operator's comfort, cabin size, ventilation and temperature. Alternatively, a noise refuge may be provided for the operator when not working at the machine - such a refuge is suitable where an operator has no fixed working position.

- Use of quiet machines and processes

Noise control should be taken into account when deciding which of different processes is to be used. When appropriate, machines should be supported on anti-vibration mountings, i.e. metal to metal impact should be eliminated where possible.

- Community noise nuisance

Due regard should be paid to the need for avoiding the creation of noise (nuisance) in nearby or community property.

- Reduction of exposure duration

It may be possible to avoid excessive noise exposure of employees by reducing the duration of exposure. Suggested measures include job rotation or re-arrangement of work (job design) to allow part of the work to be carried out in a quiet setting. Where appropriate rest rooms should be separated from noisy areas by effective sound insulation.

The question of personal protection of the employee is normally thought of as a last resort. Personal protection refers to the supply and use of ear muffs or protectors. Effective ear protection should be provided on an individual basis, and should never be used as a substitute for effective noise control. Provided adequate protection is given it is preferable for the wearers to be allowed a personal choice among different protectors.

A major text in the whole area, although oldish, remains Burns and Robinson (1970) [41].

4.3.7 Records

It is now common practice in UK industries where noise is a major problem to maintain records of persons employed and ear protection, and of general noise surveys [32]. Records enable ear protection and noise reduction areas to be determined.

General records should include:

- department and place in which readings were taken
- number of persons normally employed in the place concerned
- Leq, if calculated
- instruments used in survey
- date of calibration of such instruments
- range of sound levels recorded
- date on which measurements were taken
- other relevant information (e.g. processes taking place).

Personal records (of ear protection used) should include:

- name of person
- job, department and place at which the person works-
  type of ear protection issued
- date of issue of ear protection where appropriate
- other relevant information (e.g. age of worker)

Given below are examples of the recommended record forms [32].

4.4 ASBESTOS

4.4.1 Reporting and notifying criteria

First, it must be pointed out this section on asbestos is based upon the latest information, guidance and proposed legislation for health and safety, with respect to asbestos in the UK. The latter is encompassed within the 1984 Health and Safety Commission (HSC) Consultative Document [42], the contents of which are still being disucussed by those concerned. Procedures for notification of asbestos - related diseases were implicitly outlined in Chapters 2 and 3.

With regard to notification of exposure, there is a requirement that all work activities where workers are regularly exposed above the action level are to be notified to the Health and Safety Executive (HSE). The use of action levels is a central feature of the proposed Regulations, and is a familiar concept in occupational hygiene. It is a device to ensure that, on the one hand, additional precautions are taken when the level of risk justifies it, and on the other that such precautions are not applied where they are not necessary. This requirement of notification of regular exposure is not provided for in the existing legislation, other than for work involving crocidolite or covered by the Asbestos (Licensing) Regulations 1983 [43], and is a requirement on a once-and-for-all basis, unless circumstances change.

1. RECORD OF SOUND LEVELS

    i)   name of occupier -
    ii)   address of 'factory' -
    iii) date of survey -
    iv)   department(s) -
    v)   particulars of sound levels recorded -

(1) Place	(2) Number Employed	(3) Max dB(A)	(4) Min dB(A)	(5) Leq	(6) Ear protection area (Y/N)

    vi)   comments (e.g. relevant to conditions at time of survey, or type of noise) -
    vii) instruments used:-
      + type(s) -
      + date of last calibration -

Signature:

Date:

2. RECORD OF PERSONAL EAR PROTECTION

Name of occupier -

Address of 'factory' -

(1) Name of Person employed	(2) Job, Dept. and place of work	(3) Type of ear Protection	(4)* Date of Issue	(5)* Signature of Employee

* Entries in (4) and (5) not required where ear protection is of the disposable type.

In the proposed Regulations there will be a new legal requirement covering medical surveillance and occupational health records. The aim is to enable early detection of any ill effects of exposure to asbestos, to allow appropriate health information to be given to employees and to secure the collection, storage and use of data (for the detection of hazards and control measure assessment). Such regulations will require the keeping of occupational health records for employees exposed above the action level.

The 'Control of Asbestos at Work' proposals state that work activities where persons are likely to be exposed to asbestos dust in excess of the action level laid down must be notified (to the HSE) in writing at least twenty eight days before the work commences. Generally, a single notification of the work activity will meet the requirements, and it will not be necessary to notify each individual job involving asbestos or materials containing asbestos where the action level is likely to be exceeded.

For the manufacturing industry written notification will have to include brief details of the types of products produced at the particular workplace subject to notification. Also, a new notification should be made if there is an important change in the work on asbestos (or asbestos-containing materials), whatever industry is concerned.

Employers holding a licence under the 1983 Asbestos (licensing) Regulations to carry out work with asbestos and are doing so according to the terms and conditions of the licence need not submit additional notification of that work.

It should be noted that these proposed notification procedures (or more precisely Regulations) are expected to become operative in December 1985 or as soon as possible thereafter. The proposed Asbestos (Prohibition) Regulations project is expected to be completed in 1985 or thereafter.

A similarly thorough recording procedure is required for the results of air monitoring, and these records are to last for as long as the individual occupational health records to which they relate are retained.

For the medical surveillance of employees exposed to asbestos, all employees will be medically examined before they begin work with asbestos and subsequently at least once every two years for as long as they work with asbestos.

4.4.2 Relevant general and specific legislation

According to the statutory definition, "asbestos" means any of the following minerals - crocidolite, amosite, chrysolite, fibrous anthophylite and any mixture containing any of those minerals. Thus, asbestos is a general term for a number of silicates of iron, magnesium, calcium, sodium and aluminium, and occurs as a natural fibre.

In terms of general legislation and obligations the Health and Safety at Work etc. Act (HASAWA) 1974 requires every employer to ensure, so far as is reasonably practicable, the health, safety and welfare at work of all employees. This duty extends to protecting employees from the inherent risks of asbestos. Both employers, the self-employed and occupiers must conduct their undertakings and keep their premises in such a way as to ensure that others are also not exposed to risk. The effect of the provisions of the HASAWA is to make every employer and business organisation responsible for asbestos exposure risks. Compliance with the regulations and any approved codes of practice will help ensure fulfilment of the general HASAWA duties.

Current specific legislation exists for asbestos, (e.g. Asbestos Regulations,1969, SI No 690); however, the situation is at present under review. As was mentioned earlier, the consultative document Control of Asbestos at Work : Draft Regulations and draft Approved Code of Practice outlines the

UK's position in 1985. Although the HASAWA 1974 covers all work activities the requirements are so general that the obligations on employers and employees are not always clearly understood.

The Asbestos Regulations 1969 cover only those premises which fall within the definition of a factory in the Factories Act 1961. The requirements in these regulations are considered not wholly appropriate for certain circumstances in which there is the exposure of workers to asbestos; for example, construction, demolition, etc. Also, the Asbestos Regulations 1969 are fairly strict and limited in prescribing the methods by which control is to be achieved. Furthermore, they do not take into account the developments in knowledge and technology.

So, the HSC's proposals for comprehensive regulations, supported by an Approved Code of Practice were made [42]. The proposals are intended to implement provision of the two European Community (E.C.) Directives on asbestos. These are 83/477/EEC on the protection of workers from the risks related to exposure to asbestos at work, and 83/478/EEC on the labelling provisions on the marketing and use of asbestos.

The objectives of the regulations are

- to provide one set of regulations covering all work activities involving asbestos;
- to implement those recommendations of the Advisory Committee on Asbestos (ACA) which relate to work activities and are not covered by existing or other proposed legislation; and;
- to enable the Asbestos Regulations 1969 to be revoked.

In the development of the proposals the HSE gave consideration to whether duties should be absolute or qualified by the common "practicable" or "reasonably practicable". Most of the draft regulations are cast in terms of absolute duties, as are the Asbestos Regulations 1969. The regulations will apply to all work activities involving asbestos from which exposure of persons to asbestos may arise. Such work might include, as well as the manufacture and processing, installation, maintenance or removal of asbestos products, the handling, storage, distribution, disposal, etc. of asbestos-containing materials.

The proposed regulations introduce for the first time a specific requirement to carry out air monitoring to assess compliance with the control limits and the duty to minimize exposure and, where appropriate, for the purposes of assessment. Also, for the first time, the regulations place duties on employers to give specific information to their employees and persons affected by their work activities on asbestos. The importance of adequate information, instruction and training was emphasised by the HSC's Working Groups on asbestos.

There are two aspects to the setting of the action level; these are

- the averaging period, and
- the dust concentration.

For types of asbestos other than amosite and crocidolite the proposed action level lies between the following:

- averaging periods between 4 hours and 3 months
- dust concentrations between O.I fibre/ml and 0.25 fibre/ml.

The proposal for amosite and crocidolite is 0.1 fibres/ml, whilst the averaging period is not yet decided.

The proposed regulations would revoke the Asbestos Regulations 1969 (which are currently in operation) when they come into effect in December of this year. Also, certain parts of the Asbestos (Licensing) Regulations 1983 will be revoked.

4.4.3 Statistical information

From the HSC's "Control of Asbestos at Work" [42] the
following information was given on the effects of
exposure/incidence of disease with asbestos at work. The
Advisory Committee on Asbestos (ACA) [44] found that there was
a causal relationship between exposure to asbestos and disease
with respect to asbestosis', pleural thickening', lung cancer
and mesothelioma (cancer of pleura and peritoneum).
Also, it concluded that there was a link between exposure to
certain types of asbestos and cancer of the larynx and
gastro-intestinal tract.

Numbers	
asbestos with lung cancer	79
asbestos with mesothelioma	131
asbestos alone or with another disease	60
* Total Asbestos:	270
mesothelioma of pleura	296
mesothelioma of peritoneum	22
mesothelioma of pleuras and peritoneum	5
mesothelioma, site not specific	122
* Total mesothelioma:	445

* Note - both totals include deaths where both asbestosis
  and mesothelioma are mentioned.

The above table shows the number of death certificates
mentioning the causes of death most certainly related to
asbestos for 1981, the latest year for which figures are
available.

Generally, information on the incidence of these diseases
is limited and is complicated by the possibility of
mis-diagnosis and by the difficulty of establishing a link
with occupational exposure to asbestos, particularly in the
case of lung cancer.

Figures for previous years do not exhibit any discernible trend towards a reduction in the number of deaths, although it is quite likely that improvements in control (e.g. 1969 Asbestos Regulations) are not yet reflected in these figures.

It must also be borne in mind that the numbers of death certificates quoted are likely to be a gross underestimate of total deaths from asbestos-related disease. Additionally, no consideration is given to morbidity where death has not yet occurred or has been from other causes.

A considerable number of mortality and follow-up studies can be found reported in the British Journal of Occupational Medicine.

4.4.4 Compensation Criteria

The question of compensation for asbestos-related disease(s) falls within the realms of the State's Industrial Injuries Benefits Scheme. As was outlined in Chapter 2, the IIBS also deals with prescribed industrial diseases. The benefit under the scheme for pneumoconiosis and byssinosis is disablement benefit. The term pneumoconiosis includes asbestosis and silicosis. Thus, a claim for benefit as a result of suffering from asbestosis is dealt with under the rules concerning pneumoconiosis.

The claimant will qualify for disablement benefit for pneumoconiosis if:

- a medical board of specialist doctors decide that the claimant is suffering from the disease as it is defined in the Social Security Act 1975, and at some time since 4 July 1948 the claimant has worked:
  - in one of the prescribed dusty occupations known to carry a risk of the disease (ie exposure to asbestos dust)
  - in any other dusty occupation, provided that the claimant has never at any time worked in a prescribed one.

In this case, the claimant will be asked for a medical certificate to support the claim.

The claim must be made on the social security claim form Bl 100 (Pn).

If the claimant has satisfied the past employment criteria then a chest X-ray is arranged by the pneumoconiosis panel. Also, occupational and medical history is taken into account and the panel decides if the claim is to be allowed. (If the X-rays reveal no trace of the disease, then the claim will be disallowed.) The pneumoconiosis medical board assesses the degree of disablement resulting from the asbestosis and the claimant will be entitled to a disablement pension based on that assessment.

Assessment is made by comparing the condition as a result of the disease with that of a normal healthy person the same age and sex as the claimant. The medical board may make an increased assessment if the claimant suffers from some other condition which makes the disablement more disabling than it would otherwise be. Normally, the assessment applies to a limited period of time after which the claimant must be re-examined and re-assessed.

Disablement benefit for asbestosis is paid as a weekly pension related to the assessment of disablement. The current rates of the pension are given in the DHSS leaflet NI 196, whilst the issue of industrial injuries benefits paid for pneumoconiosis and byssinosis is covered in the DHSS leaftlet NI 3 [45].

The prescribed industrial disease D3 (previously no 44) refers to "diffuse mesothelioma (primary neoplasm of the mesothelium of the pleura or of the pericardium or of the peritoneum). A cancer starting in the covering of the lungs or the lining of the abdomen." The occupations for which this disease is prescribed is as follows:
any occupation involving -

    (i)   the handling of working of asbestos or any admixture of asbestos; or

(ii)   the manufacture or repair of asbestos textiles or other articles containing or composed of asbestos; or

(iii)   the cleaning of any machines or plant used in any of the foregoing operations and of any chambers, fixtures and appliances for the collection of asbestos dust; or

(iv)   substantial exposure to the dust arising from any of the foregoing opeerations.

The conditions relating to entitlement to benefits for diffuse mesothelioma (D3) are, along with the other prescribed diseases, outlined in the DHSS leaflet NI 2 [37] (December 1984).

It is worth noting that the Society for the Prevention of Asbestosis and Industrial Diseases (SPAID) has long maintained that many workers have been denied their rightful compensation because of the current ruling that asbestosismust be shown to be present.

Adequate (ie HSE-approved) and suitable respiratory protective equipment should be provided by employers for any employee who is exposed to asbestos at work, according to SPAID.

4.4.5   Inspection procedures

Only through the use of an electron microscope, which is not generally available, can an accurate picture of the amount of asbestos trapped in the lungs be obtained. Without such sophisticated equipment, many cases of asbestosis remain undiagnosed, suppression are not reasonably practicable, containment of asbestos in totally closed systems, preferably under negative pressure, or in enclosed containers;
- where totally closed systems are not reasonably practicable, partial enclosure with effective local exhaust ventilation being used;

- where no form of enclosure is reasonably practicable, by effective local exhaust ventilation as close to the source of asbestos dust as possible;
- restricting the quantity of asbestos used, limiting or where reasonably practicable, enclosing the area in the workplace in which asbestos is used and, limiting the number of people exposed.

In appropriate cases the period of exposure should be limited, but this is not a desirable option if it leads to a corresponding increase in the number of persons exposed.

Russell (1983) provides a critique of U.K. asbestos inspection procedures [46]. See Byron et al (1977) for international comparisons of the practice of asbestos fibre counting [47].

4.4.6 Prevention Measures

The HSC consultative document ("Control of Asbestos at Work") covers the area of prevention thoroughly. Draft Regulation 8 proposes the requirements for the prevention or minimisation of exposure to asbestos.

It is proposed that employers must ensure the exposure of their employees to asbestos is either completely prevented, or where prevention is not reasonably practicable, reduced to the minimum that is reasonably practicable by means other than the provision of respiratory protective equipment. Also, it is required that employees must never be exposed to concentrations of asbestos that exceed the relevant control limit.

With respect to prevention and minimisation, the institutation of work procedures which ensure that asbestos is carefully handled at all times and which encourage good hygiene standards is an essential aspect of any system of control measures. Systems of work should, therefore, aim to minimise workers' contact with raw fibre, to minimise the possiblity of spillages or accumulation of debris and to discourage careless, unduly hurried or untidy work.

The means of preventing or minimising exposure should include one or more of the following as appropriate to the circumstances:

- elimination of the asbestos or asbestos-containing material;
- substitution of asbestos by a material that is less hazardous;
- plant, processes and systems of work designed to prevent the release of or exposure to asbestos dust or to suppress the release of asbestos dust into the air;
- where elimination, substituting, prevention or exposure, or is liable to be exposed to airborne concentrations of asbestos in excess of the relevant control limit.

Generally speaking, the proposed Code will advocate that the prevention or minimisation of exposure to asbestos should be achieved by the following means:

(i) the taking of adequate steps to secure the cleanliness of workplaces, premises and plant;

(ii) prevention or minimisation of the spread of contamination;

(iii) where necessary, the provision of adequate and suitable personal protective equipment;

(iv) the provision of adequate and suitable facilities for washing, accommodation for clothing, eating and drinking.

4.5   BIBLIOGRAPHY

26. DEPARTMENT OF HEALTH AND SOCIAL SECURITY (DHSS) "Industrial injuries - INDUSTRIAL DEATH BENEFIT, for widows and other dependants." NI 10/Mar '83. London: HMSO. 1983 pp7.

As the title suggests this DHSS leaflet covers industrial death benefit - yet does so in a thorough manner. Clearly written information for claimants.

27. HEALTH AND SAFETY EXECUTIVE (HSE).   "Fatal accidents in construction 1978". HM Factory Inspectorate Report.   London: HMSO, 1981 pp16.

This report summarises in four tables the type and the distribution of fatal accidents in the construction industry for 1978.   Specifically discussed are falls, accidents with machinery such as cranes and hoists, and accidents involving particular types of construction work.

28. HSE "Construction.   Health and Safety 1981-82" London: HMSO. 1983.   pp87.

Prepared by the Construction National Industry Groups which deals with the hazards to safety and health in the construction industry.   This is the latest report for this area and contains, amongst others, important and recent information on falls from heights.   Provides a good review of the construction industry's approach to health and safety matters.

29. MANNING, D. Slips and Falls.   Occupational Safety and Health.   July, 15-19.   1981 (5 pp).

A bibliographic and statistical survey of literature on slipping and falling accidents.   Gaps in current knowledge are outlined.

30. HSE "Preventing falls to window cleaners."   IND(S)4(L) M40 S/84; and"Working as fragile roofs" IND (G) 21 (L). Published by the HSE 1984.

Leaflet giving information to window cleaners on falls and safety measures.

31. HSE "Roofwork - prevention of falls."   Guidance note GS10.   London: HMSO. 1983.
A useful note with practical guidance on the prevention of falls during roof work. Note also GS15 in the Guidance series dealing with general access scaffolds.

32. DEPARTMENT OF EMPLOYMENT (D.E.). "Code of Practice for reducing the exposure of employed persons to Noise." Her Majesty's Stationery office (HMSO): London. 1972. 33pp

This Code is probably the most often referred to booklet in the area of noise in industry. Although published in 1972, this clearly- written voluntary Code of Practice is currently applicable in the absence of specific noise regulations for many situations. The work of Burns and Robinson (1970) provide the basis for the Code.

33. HEALTH AND SAFETY COMMISSION (H.S.C.). "Protection of hearing at work". HSC Consultative Document. London: HMSO. July 1981.

Represents an up-date of the DE voluntary Code in the form of general provisions and proposed Regulations.

34. COMMISSION FOR THE EUROPEAN COMMUNITIES. "Amended proposal for a draft directive on noise". O.J.C. 214/84. 1984.
This amendment to the proposal of O.J.C. 289/82 sets limits for peak sound pressure (200 Pa), daily sound exposure level (90 dB(A)), the provision of hearing protectors and audiometric examination (daily exposure level of 85 dB (A)) for employed persons. Future reduction of the mandatory daily level to 85 dB (A) is discussed. There is opposition to this proposal from sections of U.K. industry.

35. TEMPEST, W. Noise exposure and hearing loss. Annals of Occupational Hygiene, 21, 51-56, 1978 (6 pp)

A critique of the inappropriate nature of existing standards to provide complete protection for workers, or for employers open to common law claims. Uses individual cases and derived noise-induced hearing loss audiograms for long-term exposure workers.

35a ACTON, W.I. Can noise cause accidents? Occupational Safety and Health September, 14-16. 1982 (3pp).

Reviews arguments for and against the proposition that the effects of noise may be implicated in certain types of Occupational accident.

36. DEPARTMENT OF HEALTH AND SOCIAL SECURITY (DHSS). "Occupational deafness. New rules - more people are now eligible for benefit." Leaflet NI.207/Mar 84. (Replaces edition of Oct 83.) London: HMSO.

Well written leaflet by the DHSS giving the latest rules concerning benefit claims for occupational deafness. (See also leaflet NI.196, in Chapter 3 bibliography, which details the latest DHSS benefit rates.)

37. DEPARTMENT OF HEALTH AND SOCIAL SECURITY (DHSS) "Prescribed Industrial Diseases." NI 2/Dec '84. London: HMSO. 1984. pp11.

A DHSS guidance booklet which includes coverage of the criteria and procedures for claiming benefits in respect of industrial diseases (prescribed), in simple language.

38. ACTON, W.I. and GRIME R.P. Noise and hearing loss compensation. Am. Occup. Hyg. Vol 23, p. 205-215, 1980.

Discusses the two ways in which noise-induced injury may be compensated in G.B., taking examples from recent high court judgements.

39. DEPARTMENT OF HEALTH AND SOCIAL SECURITY (D.H.S.S.). "Report on Occupational Deafness." Cmnd 8749. November 1982. London: HMSO.

A comprehensive report by the Industrial Advisory Council in accordance with section 141 of the Social Security Act 1975, on the operation of the provisions for occupational deafness and on whether these should be extended.

40. HEALTH AND SAFETY EXECUTIVE (H.S.E.). "100 practical applications of noise reduction methods." London: Her Majesty's Stationery office (HMSO). 1983. 112pp.

This report by HM Factory Inspectorate details ways in which noise can be reduced at source by the application of engineering solutions. This is achieved by UK case study examples, e.g. pneumatics, acoustic guards. Although a guide and not making detailed specifications, noise reduction methods are indicated which might be achieved with application and expertise.

41. BURNS, W. and ROBINSON, D.W. "Hearing and Noise in Industry".Department of Health and Social Security (D.H.S.S.). London: HMSO. 1970. 241pp.

'Hearing and noise in industry' is the most significant piece of research into the noise-related problems of industry yet. It remains a valuable work of reference (and possibly will do for years ahead). The major text, and sixteen appendices by the authors and their collaborators, describes a Medical Research Council (MRL) / National Physical Laboratory (NPL) project of fundamental research.

42. HEALTH AND SAFETY COMMISSION (HSC) "Control of Asbestos at Work." Draft Regulations and Draft Code of Practice. Consultative Document. London: Her Majesty's Stationery Office. 1984. pp65.

The 'Control of Asbestos at Work' is a comprehensive document which describes what will probably be accepted in terms of specific legislation and an Approved Code of Practice. It is the most recent HSC or HSE document concerned with asbestos and deals with virtually all aspects of occupational asbestos (the major exception is the licensing regulations).

43. HEALTH AND SAFETY EXECUTIVE (HSE) "A guide to the Asbestos (Licensing) Regulations 1983." Health and Safety Series booklet HS(R)19. London: HMSO. 1984. pp27.

Simply a brief account of the Licensing Regulations for asbestos, including details on applications for licenses. Although the guidance is based on legal requirements, it is not intended as an authoritative interpretation of the law, (such an interpretation can only be made by the courts).

44. HEALTH AND SAFETY COMMISSION (HSC) "Asbestos," Volume 1: Final Report of the Advisory Committee. Volume 2: - papers commissioned by the committee. London: Her Majesty's Stationery Office. 1979. Vol 1 pp100; Vol 2 pp103.

These volumes provide a detailed account of the Advisory Committee on Asbestos (ACA) which was presented to the HSC. As such, it forms the basis, in terms of recommendations, for more recent proposals and reforms. A great deal of technical detail is included although the report remains readable.

45. DEPARTMENT OF HEALTH AND SOCIAL SECURITY (DHSS) "Industrial injuries paid for Pneumonconiosis and Byssinosis." NI3/Sept '82. London: HMSO. 1983 S.

This booklet covers claim criteria and procedures guidance for occupational asbestosis sufferers in a straightforward manner.

46. Russell, J. R. Asbestos - a failure? In: Essays to commemorate 150 years of health and safety inspection: Her Majesty's Inspectors of Factories 1933-1983. HSC, 37-39, 1983.

A brief but interesting look at failures within and outside the Inspectorate in the investigation and regulation of asbestos hazards. Regards asbestos-related disease as an exceptional case.

47. BARON, P. et al. A summary of asbestos fibre counting experience in seven countries. Annals of Occupational Hygiene, 20, 321-332. 1977.

Concludes that more interaction between, and standardisation
of practices of, different agencies in different countries is
required.

CHAPTER 5   MORTALITY AND MORBIDITY STUDIES

5.1 Occupational Accidents and Diseases in the UK

5.1.1. Reporting procedures & Statistical Analysis

Eleven years on from the HASAWA, the general picture as regards accident and disease in the U.K. is far from satisfactory, although it may appear favourable in comparison with other countries.   Certainly, fatality rates have fallen.   In addition, accident reporting suggests a reduction of about 30% of lost time accidents from 1975-84.   It must be borne in mind, however, that these figures still fluctuate quite considerably, although not as much as in the early '70s.   More important is the persistent inadequacy of report-ing procedures, and specifically the way in which statistical information about accidents is calculated and computed.   Even before the 1974 Act, Powell et al's (1971) Report "2000 Accidents" drew attention to this problem [48]. This study, undertaken by the National Institute of Industrial Psychology (NIIP) with the joint support of the Ministries of Technology, and Labour (now Depts. of Trade and Industry, and Employment respectively), concerned itself with 2,367 accidents at work which occurred in four different types of industry over a period of two years.   Nearly fifteen years later, however, the problems it identified regarding reporting procedures and statistical analysis, have remained essentially unresolved.

The most common indices used in U.K. accident assessment are as follows:

1)   Annual account of
       - first aid treatments, etc.
       - major accidents
       - fatal accidents
       - 'lost time' accidents

2)   The accident incidence rate per thousand persons employed, represented by

no. of reportable* accidents x 1000
    no. of persons at risk

(*notifiable can be substituted)

3)   The accident frequency rate:

Freq. = 'lost time' accidents x 100,000
        man-hours worked

Note that the definition of "lost time"/"more than 3 day" etc. accidents causes problems, as does changing the criteria for lost time, etc.

4)   Accident severity rate -

= man hours lost x 100,000
 man hours worked

In an Accident Preventive Advisory Unit (APAU) document entitled "Managing Safety", the way in which statistics are employed was again commented upon.   They suggested longer periods (i.e. several years) for accident review periods so that real trends could be analysed and statistical reliability improved [49].   In addition, the Robens Committee stated that there still existed a substantial amount of under-reporting of legally notifiable accidents in the U.K. [1].

Beaumont (1980) conducted one of the few inter-industry examinations of variations in accident rates [50].   He looked at accident rates within the manufacturing sector in Britain with particular reference to a number of the leading hypotheses generated by this debate over the respective roles of job and worker characteristics in accident causation.   His results are sufficiently encouraging to warrant further research using the basic model he proposes.

A number of references relevant to the statistical analysis of accident data have already been presented in the bibliography of chapter 2.

5.1.2 The Role of the Factory Inspectorate and EMAS

Since 1974 the workload of the Factory Inspectorate has increased enormously with over 250,000 visits and more than 17,000 accidents investigated per year. This has inevitably reduced traditional visiting and has had implications for the role of the factory inspector. The increasing complexity of industrial processes and the use of chemicals creating more toxic hazards has lead to the development fo a specialised capacity within the Factory Inspectorate. But as the technical base of industry is changing, so too is the public perception of risk, and thus a frequent reappraisal of their programmes are needed. Reductions on F.I. manpower (although about to be reversed to some extent) have further exacerbated the stretching of their resources.

An article produced in 1980 by Warburton, the director of ROSPA, analyses the Factory Inspectorate's changing role, particularly with regard to balancing the enforcement and advisory aspects of their job and the need for self regulation in health, safety and industry [51]. He notes that accidents are caused more by a "failure to maintain than a failure to provide, and stresses that the human value factors in accident causation have not been sufficiently considered - to that extent section 2 of the Health and Safety at Work Act is of very direct relevance". He recommends a four-part approach of equal relevance to Inspectors, employers and employees'.

1. high standards of physical safeguards and protective devices should be applied and maintained.
2. more compliance with statute law.
3. the commitment and understanding of management to the relevance of Health and Safety within their other management aims.
4. the participation and involvement of the workforce.

See [52] for information on the activities of EMAS.

Since the mid-1970's there has been a spread of worker participation in health and safety, for example in the form of collective bargaining at the workplace level and the appointment of full-time trade union officials, nationally and regionally, responsible for health and safety. However, unions have come under criticism for their emphasis on compensation after the event rather than prevention before. Two years after Warburton's Factory Inspectorate recommendations [51], Glendon and Booth (1982) provided a useful review of worker participation in occupational health and safety in Britain [53].

5.1.3 Occupational Health Services

Most occupational health services in the U.K. today are in private industry. The remainder of the working sector, namely the self-employed or those in smaller companies (about half) have virtually no cover apart from the limited advisory services of the HSE. To quote McKinnon (1982) "In theory, assistance can always be sought from EMAS, but the service is understaffed and in many cases employers tend to identify it with the Factory Inspectorate, which for some, still retains a somewhat forbidding image" [54]. There have been a few co-operative group schemes in the U.K. but they have proved difficult to finance and have had little impact. This means in effect that 50% of the population are omitted from epidemiological surveys.

In general private occupational health services are hierarchical with doctors at the top. There are some very successful examples, but there are two disadvantages. These are that it is expensive and tends to inhibit the development of the service if no doctor can be found. Furthermore it encourages clinical and therapeutic procedures at the expense of primary prevention, and tends to separate health from safety, which is not compatible with the multi disciplinary nature of occupational health, nor with the original aims of the Health and Safety Act. McDonald (1981) points out that present legislation copes poorly with chronic and delayed effects of occupational exposure [55]. He also notes that the NHS has yet to make comprehensive provision for its own employees, let along accept responsibility for any aspect of occupational health. He also cites Kinnersley's (1973) quote that injury to a worker is "one example of the conflict of interest between workers and employers when it comes to health and safety. The conflict exists because safety is paid for out of profits [3]. McDonald proposes a new formula, the main points of which are:

1. a new understanding between employers and employees to reduce conflict of interest.
2. a basic occupational health service for all employuees (e.g. periodic health screening).
3. a national framework for epidemiological research and surveillance.
4. a national policy for appropriately trained personnel.

5.1.4 Industrial disease

The question of industrial disease in the U.K. presents an even more complex picture, owing to the difficulty of identifying such diseases and the time lag in their emergence after exposure. Although the basic research in this area is medical, the Factory Inspectorate has a vital role in indicating useful directions of research from its knowledge of working conditions, and especially of how and where workers may be exposed to potentially dangerous materials. Prior to 1972, the Medical Branch of the inspectorate provided a link between this body of experience and the medical profession. Since 1972, these have been merged into EMAS. The role of EMAS and a description of their 1976 survey of occupational health services in a sample of workplaces in the U.K., is described in a document by the Health and Safety Commission entitled "Occupational health Services: the way ahead" (1978) [56].

Certain diseases, most of them resulting from poisoning and chronic in nature, are notifiable under the Factories Act. The number of cases notified, never large, has been sharply reduced in recent years, from over 200 a year in the early 1970s to 110 in 1978, and 65 in 1979. These diseases are also all "prescribed" for the purposes of the industrial injuries scheme which is the main source of information on the incidence of industrial diseases.

A large proportion of all serious occupational disease is respiratory in nature. Unless there is better early identification of respiratory disorders, causal factors and early control of industrial processes, future health and economic costs will markedly increase.

Certain diseases have long been linked with certain occupations. But with the increasing use of synthetic materials has come the realisation that some materials and conditions of work increase liability to diseases which are not exclusively occupational in character - for example, bronchitis, dermatitis, allergic conditions and some cancers.

Since using lists of noxious substances in the 1950's, in British legal actions reliance as regards occupational hygiene standards has generally been placed on TLVs (Threshold Limit Values) which have been continuously republished since 1962. In 1968 the British Occupational Hygiene Society (BOHS) was set up. The BOHS hygiene standards have no fixed structure or range of content but normally include:

1. the standard of exposure
2. the health data from which it is derived
3. the probable degree of protection the standard affords.
4. information on the different hygiene sampling procedures and the interpretation of results.
5. recommendations for medical surveillance.

Thomas (1979) provides a useful analysis of BOHS and compares it with the standards of other organisations and institutes [57]. In particular he considers the defining of the health effect on which to base a standard, the problem of data acquisition, and the occurrence of factors in the work situation, or in workers themselves, which can modify the protection given by standards.

5.1.5 HSC - Future Plan of Work

One of the priorities of the HSC 1983/4 plan of work [2] related to the main types of hazard - (a) events leading to immediate injury, (b) hazards resulting in acute or long-term damage to health, and (c) major hazards. The problem with (a) is not the shortage of existing legislation but the fact that much of the older legislation is outdated by technological change. The areas they intend to concentrate on in the next few years are coal mines, docks, electricity and flammable and explosive substances.

With regard to (b) the existing legislation is fragmentary and deals with particular substances. The future aim is a more comprehensive framework for control of these hazards, particularly in the areas of toxic chemicals, radiation hazards and noise.

For the third area, (c) an effective programme for these "low probability events which have a potential for disaster" is crucial.

After the Flixborough accident in 1974, the HSC appointed a committee of experts, the Advisory Committee on Major Hazards (ACMH) to consider the problem and make recommendations. Following the publication by the ACMH of a number of reports to this end, the HSC intended to implement their proposals for notification and hazard surveys in a single set of regulations [58]. However as a result of developments within the EC this programme was changed.

In June, 1982 the European Directive on the major accident hazards of certain industrial activities was finally adopted, and the Control of Industrial Major Accident Hazards (CIMAH) Regulations implemented in the U.K., complementing the existing Regulations, as well as the changes in planning controls which government departments responsible for planning in England, Scotland and Wales are developing.

The principle objectives of the CIMAH Regulations are "the prevention of major accidents arising from industrial activities, the limitation of the effects of such accidents both on man and on the environment, and the harmonisation of control measures to prevent and limit major accidents in the EC" [59].

An accident is defined as major if it meets the following conditions:

(a)   that it leads to a serious danger to man or the environment, and
(b)   that it results from uncontrolled developments in the course of an "industrial activity", and
(c)   that it involves one or more "Dangerous substances".

A detailed guide to the CIMAH regulations can be found in the HS(R) 21 booklet, quoted above, from which a timetable for manufacturers' compliance and a guide for them can be found [59].

While the risks of major hazards are not new the situation has become more serious. The move in recent years to huge increases in plant size and complexity, coupled with the tendency of high hazard industries to bunch together in complexes where one accident can trigger a domino effect, necessitate the development of sophisticated techniques of risk assessment in the future.

Nuclear and military installations, explosives, mining, quarrying and waste disposal sites are excluded from the scope of the Regulations, as are dangerous substances being transported by vehicle or vessel to or from the site of an industrial activity. Priorities in the field of nuclear installations are:

(i) the continuing evaluation of the design of the pressurised water reactor and

(ii) the ongoing monitoring of safety in the fuel - reprocessing installations of BNFL.

An effective framework for the transport of hazardous materials does not yet exist and urgent action is needed in this area.

5.2 Group of Workers/Age Groups

5.2.1 Occupational accidents and disabled employees

In past studies of accidents at work (reported in Kettle, 1984 [60]), a common finding has been that the accident rates of disabled workers were no worse than the rates for able-bodied workers. In fact, they were often found to be lower. In the U.K. there is a requirement that employers employ no less than 3% (known as the quota). However, it is true that the quota only applies to registered disabled and does not take account of the many other disabled workers who are not registered (Taylor and Burridge, 1981 [61]).

The results of an investigation into the issue of occupational accidents and disabled workers, commissioned by the Health and Safety Executive, were published in 1984 [60]. A comparison was made between the accident rates of able-bodied workers and the accident rates of the disabled workers. The findings of the study were very much in accord with the findings of other studies on the issue. Using the definition of the disabled given in the Disabled Persons

(Employment) Act 1944 a sample of 3028 disabled employees, from several companies, was used. This represented nine per cent of the total average workforce. The study examined accidents and absences sustained by disabled employees.

A sorting operation of all medical records of all employees was undertaken in order to produce accurate listings of both registered and unregistered disabled workers. Similarly, the accident records were thoroughly surveyed. The accident data were analysed for each company for one year with respect to the type of accident and whether the "victim" was able-bodied or disabled. An examination of every accident that was recorded, and not just those sustained by disabled workers or those that were reportable by law, was made.

It was found, in general, that disabled workers sustained proportionally fewer accidents than able-bodied workers, lending support to the view that, given an environment that takes note of the limitations, if any, imposed by disability, disabled workers generally are less likely than other workers to sustain accidents at work. Thus, the idea that the disabled worker represents a safety hazard receives no support from the experience of the six employers in Kettle's HSE retrospective study [60].

The study also showed that disabled people could be found in all sectors of a company's workforce i.e. a particular disability, it seems does not automatically preclude particular forms of work. Also, there was little evidence to suggest that disabled workers tend to be found in one occupation more than any other.

5.2.2 Women Workers

It can be argued that a great deal needs to be done to improve the lot of women at work. The absence of knowledge and the lack of communication of information regarding the special health problems of women workers are criticisms that can be justifiably levelled at some employers. It is a great paradox that women, who are on average healthier than men and survive more illness, are often the first group of workers to be excluded from a particular occupation because of the risks involved.

The laws which require men and women to be treated differently at work are generically referred to as protective legislation. When the Health and Safety at Work Act 1974 became law it was clear that the anomalies in legislation affecting women would have to be reviewed. Under Section 55 of the Sex Discrimination Act 1975 the Health and Safety Commission (HSC) and the Equal Opportunities Commission (EOC) were given the responsibility to carry out the review. However, owing to lack of agreement between some employers and unions over the desirability of implementing the recommendations of the review, the position remains deadlocked.

It is likely that the next development will be either an HSC discussion document or draft Regulations. Minor progress may be made as various sections of the Factories Act 1961 are replaced by comprehensive regulations under the Health and Safety at Work Act.

Forty per cent of the UK workforce are women - the growth of female employment has been one of the more significant employment trends in the last fifty years. Women are not distributed equally throughout occupations, but are concentrated in a narrow range of activities with clerical and personal service occupations, education and health accounting for two thirds of female employment, and therefore disproportionately in the service sector. This is often associated with inferior conditions at work, with insecure or part-time employment and inadequate training. The protective legislation that exists covers mainly women in the manufacturing industry, and much of it is concerned with the protection of the female reproductive system, enacted in the U.K. in 1802 and accumulating ever since (Mackay and Bishop 1984) [62].

In 1977-79 the MRC was commissioned by the Dept of Employment to research the following three issues:

1)   The nature of conflict arising from the interdependence of home and work and the specific circumstances of women's employment.

2)   The observed outcomes of this.

3)   The limitations of workplace approaches to ameliorating or solving these problems.

The study is reported and interpreted by Shimmin (1984) [63].

In 1982 the Equal Opportunities Commission in cooperation with the Ergonomics Society, the Manpower Services Commission and the British Psychological Society, held a conference on 'Women at Work'.

The May 1984 edition of 'Ergonomics' [64] reports on this conference.

5.2.3 Children and Young Persons

Health and safety legislation understandably lays great emphasis upon the need for safety consciousness, supervision and training in safer methods of work for young people. In particular, there are specific restrictions relating to the employment of children. No child under the age of thirteen can be employed in any

A child is defined as a person under school leaving age (i.e. at present under 16). A young person is a person who has ceased to be a child but who has not attained 18 years of age.

The prohibitions set out below are general, applying to shops, offices, and factories. It is forbidden to employ any child in any of the following circumstances:

- where the child is under the age of 13;

- before 7.00 a.m. or after 7.00 p.m. on any day;

- for more than 2 hours on any school day;

- for more than 2 hours on Sunday; and,
- to lift, carry or move anything heavy enough to cause injury.

In addition, there is the specific provision that no child can be employed in an industrial undertaking i.e. mines, quarries, factories, building and works of engineering, construction and transportation (Employment of Women, Young Persons and Children Act 1920).

By the same Act, persons under 18 are prohibited from working in the following processes and occupations:-

(a)   asbestos processes;

(b)   blasting operations;

(c)   work with cellulose solutions or inflammable liquids containing more than 15% of benzene;

(d)   chrome processes or nitro or amido processes;

(e)   work as a crane driver;

(f)   electrolytic chromium processes;

(g)   (i)   any lead process;

      (ii)   work in any room where manipulation of raw oxide of leador pasting is carried out;

(h)   work with material not having undergone disinfection for horsehair processes;

(i)   (i)   fume processes;

      (ii)   employment in a room where fume processes are carried on (persons under 16);

      (iii)   lead processes (males under 16, females under 18);

(j)   work with unsealed radioactive substances;

(k)   scaling, surfing, or cleaning of boilers, combustion chambers etc.

(l)   any enamelling process;

(m)   manipulation if yarn dyed by lead compound; and

(n)   work in the pottery industry.

5.2.4 Y.T.S. (Youth Training Scheme)

In 1983 the Health and Safety (Youth Training Scheme) Regulations have been made to clarify the status of trainees and ensure their safety is adequately protected. The Regulations have the effect of requiring that no distinction is made between YTS trainees and employees with respect to any safety or welfare-related provisions which employers are required to make for their employees.

The Regulations were drawn up because HSC believed it to be anomalous for people who were employees (i.e. working under contract of employment) and YTS trainees (who were not) to be covered by different actions of the Health and Safety at Work Act 1974, as a result of their different employment status, even though they might be working alongside each other.

Prior to the 1983 Regulations the problem of the statutory duties not covering all providers of training work experience schemes under YTS, was a cause for concern. Also, there were other distinctions between trainees and employees concerning safety - related issues besides the precise nature of employers' duty of care towards them.

Now, under the 1983 Regulations (which came into effect in 1984), all YTS trainees are deemed to be employees "of the person whose undertaking is the provider of training at the relevant time", for the purposes of all safety legislation, except with respect to courses at educational establishments. They do not affect the status of trainees with regard to employment protection legislation. The Regulations have the effect of

-   allowing YTS trainees to be represented by an appointed safety representative and thus have the facility for making complaints on injuries;
-   ensuring that YTS trainees have the full benefit of welfare facilities at the establishments where they are placed;

- requiring that the employers' statement of health and safety policy is brought to the attention of YTS trainees in the same way as it is brought to the attention of all new employees;

- placing trainees under statutory duty, in the same way as employees are, to co-operate with providers of training or work experience in their efforts to ensure the safety of their employees/trainees.

It should be noted that the HSC has announced that it intends to conduct a full review of the position under health and safety legislation of students at colleges and of other trainees.

5.3 Technological Developments

5.3.1 Robotics

Modern assembly techniques, including the use of robotics, have become a reality in the last few years. It can be predicted that robots will become more sophisticated, have greater power and be used increasingly for assembly tasks possibly involving working alongside human operators. It is, therefore, appropriate that the work of assessing the implications for safety (and accidents) is given priority.

As interest in robot safety continues to grow the Robot Safety Liaison Group was established. The Group draws membership from makers, users, trade associations, trade unions and the HSE. The Group has discussed international standards as well as reviewing reports of accidents and incidents.

HSE information suggests that the attitudes to robot safety adopted in Western Europe are broadly similar. (For example, enclosures restricting access to the swept area by the robot are widely used). Accident experience has shown the necessity of safety measures for robots. However, in those cases where robots remove workers from dangerous or unpleasant working surroundings they bring significant benefits.

Unpredictable action patterns, the ability to move in free space and the possibility of reconfiguration all distinguish industrial robots from other automated plant. Potential hazards include trapping, impact, and the ejection of components - and these hazards may arise not only during the normal operation of the machine but could occur as a result of control malfunction or programming errors.

The benefits of industrial robots (such as relieving workpeople of dangerous and arduous tasks) may be accompanied by new hazards or result in placing different groups of workpeople at risk. A number of accidents involving robots have been reported in other countries and these show that a robot is least likely to cause an accident when in production. The problems seem to occur during the programming and maintenance tasks.

The automobile industry in the U.K. has had a major influence on the developments of robot safety guidelines. The resources of large companies can be used to develop safe working practices for robots but it is equally important that the smaller users also recognise the potential risks with these machines. (See [65], [66], [67], [68]).

5.3.2 Visual Display Units (VDU's)

Amongst the many options for office automation that are being developed and used today, the VDU is the most common electronic-based medium. There is already evidence of the health costs that might be associated with the movement towards VDU-based automation. These are located in four main areas - radiation and its effects, visual effects, postural effects and work design effects.

The presence of cataracts in a number of individuals involved in the operation of VDUs has been attributed to electromagnetic radiation. In a 1983 study by Cox (in: Pearce, 1984) [69], for the National Radiological Protection Board, on behalf of the Health and Safety Executive, measurements were made in all regions of the electromagnetic spectrum of the radiation emission levels from all types of VDUs manufactured and/or marketed in the U.K. It was concluded that the national and international limits for continuous occupational exposure are not being exceeded.

Concern has also been expressed about the possible epileptogenic properties of VDUs, and there have been a number of reports of facial dermatitis among VDU users, but no definite links have been established in these areas. In the HSE (1983) publication on VDUs [70] employees are asked to contact EMAS for advice if they experience problems in these areas.

Working at VDUs places an unusual combination of demands on the visual and musculoskeletal systems, and it is very likely that these complaints are correlated with workplace and workstation design variables. Unfortunately, VDTs are often introduced into the workplace without the application of appropriate ergonomics principles. The association of professional, executive and computer staffs (APEX) have also issued their own guidelines on health and safety aspects of new technology in a 1985 booklet [71].

The visual complaint most often reported by VDU operators is visual fatigue. This is caused by a number of factors including the display itself, the surrounding lighting, the workstation design, and the degree of repetitiveness of the task. In 1981, NIOSH commissioned the National Academy of

Sciences to examine the question of visual issues encountered in occupational use of VDUs. In turn the National Research Council Committee on Vision commissioned a review panel, the report of which appeared in 1983. While not conducted in the U.K., this study critically reviewed much of the literature and their findings are very relevant to the British context. Major critical comment concerning many of the field studies included:

- lack of theoretical framework
- failure to employ research designs allowing separation of VDU-related health complaints from job demand/work structure effects
- selection and sampling problems
- low and differential response rate problems
- failure to use multivariate statistical procedures.

The full findings are discussed in Vision Displays, Work and Vision, produced by the National Research Council in 1983 [72].

The overall feeling one can establish from the literature as regards the health effects of V.D.U.'s would seem, at best, to be 'not proven'. However, there is area for doubt about radiological and visual effects and effective long-term research is required urgently. In the meantime, continual awareness of, and screening for, problems are required.

5.4 Behavioural and Social Environment Studies

5.4.1 Shift work and health

Shift work is frequently considered a necessity of a modern industrial society, for three main reasons

- service to society;
- continuous process industries; and

- economic necessity (of getting the most out of the equipment before it is outmoded by better machines, newer designs or changing consumer wants).

In developing countries, surplus manpower can be more efficiently used in shift work as this can increase productivity and decrease capital costs. Although shift work has been deplored by some sections of society as inhuman and socially undesirable it is probably here to stay.

Harrington (1978) [73] critically reviewed the evidence relating to shift work practices and general health effects. He reached the conclusion that a great deal of the evidence pertaining to the ill effects of shift working was of dubious quality.

Considering that death can be sometimes construed as the end product of ill-health, it is surprising that only one mortality study of shift workers appears to have been undertaken. In 1972 Taylor and Pocock analysed 1578 deaths occurring in a 13 year period in a population of 8603 male manual workers employed with ten organisations (in [73]). Their study was carefully conducted but revealed virtually no evidence that shift workers had excessive death rates compared with the death rates of day workers. Ex-shift workers did seem to be slightly worse off than current shift workers and this might seem to imply some selecting out of the less fit workers from shift working, leaving only the fitter workers to cope with the 'abnormal' working hours.

With respect to sickness absence ('absenteeism') there appears to be little evidence to suggest that shift workers are more frequently absent from work due to sickness than day workers.

A summary of work on the field of circadian rhythms, and their relation to shift work was given by Rentos & Shepherd (1976) (in [73]). It was shown that shift work, and particulary night work, causes considerable disruption of circadian rhythms, and that individuals differ greatly in the speed at which they can adapt and that this might have an important bearing on shift work in general.

Harrington (1978) [73] proposed that some consensus had been achieved in the area of shift work in relation to performance and output or accident rates. The consensus, he proposed was in five areas:

"- performance is worse for long stints of repetitive work and best for cognitive work with high motivation;

- loss of sleep effects are greatest on the night shift and least on the afternoon shift;

- fatigue can increase errors and diminish performance but this can be offset if the motivation is great and breaks in the work are feasible;

- short cycle shift working minimises temporative adaptation and probably prevents performance adaptation as well;

- individual differences in performance are often much greater than group differences."

Two main sources of potential health risk are frequently cited by physicians concerned with health and shift work - disruption of sleeping patterns, and variations in eating habits. Worker complaints are centered on nervous disorders, gastro-intestinal disturbances, and fatigue.

No evidence exists to suggest that shift workers suffer unduly from disabling or serious psycho-neurotic disorders, neither do they appear to suffer excess absence attributed to sickness or death from neurological disease.

Some epidemiological evidence does suggest that rotating shift work may play a part in either inducing gastro-duodenal ulceration or at least exacerbating latent or pre-existing disease.

The main finding in the field of shift work and occupational disease is that there is a distinct lack of objective studies of morbidity and especially mortality. For a view of shiftwork and accidents, see [74].

5.4.2 Alcohol and Work

It is important that those involved in occupational health should distinguish between short and long term effects of alcohol consumption. Most organisations have clearly defined procedures for dealing with drunkeness amongst employees and it is likely that, where only a single incident is being considered, the patterns of the employees previous work record should be taken into consideration, since the decision is likely to be of a disciplinary rather than a medical nature.

Clearly an employee who is drunk is likely to show reduced efficiency and loss of fine motor skills. The loss of work has been shown to be as high as 70-85 days per annum, with a corresponding tendency towards frequent late arrival for work.

Overseas studies have indicated that work accident rates of twice or three times 'normal' may be found. Also, differential rates among young and middle-aged employees are apparent, and the majority of alcohol-related work accidents occur in the afternoon.

There is a considerable body of evidence from a range of sources that demonstrates that different occupations have very different rates of alcoholism. The Office of Population, Consensus and Surveys (OPCS) reviewed the evidence and, using male liver cirrhoses mortality as the best available indicator of relative alcoholism prevalence rates drew up tables of occupations.

In the U.K., the Alcohol Education Centre and Scottish Health Education Unit have produced a sophisticated multimedia resource pack to assist companies in the task of effective prevention of alcohol-related disabilities.

In 1981, the HSE, together with the Health Departments and Department of Employment published an Occasional Paper entitled "The problem drinker at work" together with the Health Departments and Department of Employment. The document sought not only to inform, but also to encourage management and trade unions to develop policies to help problem drinkers and utilised the principles of such policies [75]. A very recent review of the problem of drinkers and drinking at work is provided in [76].

5.5 Epidemiological Studies

Epidemiology, is said to be the study of the pattern of disease indicators, in terms of host, agent and environment, in a given population and the comparison of such patterns with those found in other populations. This provides an objective measurement of a population's disease experience, and an indication of the size, distribution, or severity of any disease process. Epidemiology, provides an invaluable means of measuring the extent of an occupationally related disease and the risk presented to those at work, of investigating the potential causes of accidents, and of examining accident or disease patterns after control measures have been introduced, to access their effectiveness (See [77]).

The main unit responsible for HSE epidemiology study within the U.K. is the HSE's Epidemiology and Medical Statistics Unit (EMSU). EMSU is responsible for:
-       the setting up, processing, analysis and reports of within-house epidemiological surveys;
-       the collection, maintenance, and collation of routine statistics on occupational ill health, including notifiable diseases and gassing accidents;

- the maintenance of the mesothelioma, asbestosis and
  angiosarcoma case registers; and,
- the provision of advice to other parts of the HSE on
  epidemiological matters and the assessment of work
  relevant to HSE policy.

A EMSU report on current projects is submitted (annually)
to the Medical Advisory Committee. The Employment Medical
Advisory Service (EMAS) fulfil the role of go-between with
respect to the HSE and the EMSU. As EMAS programmes form a
relatively small part of occupational epidemiology in the
U.K. there is by necessity much interaction between external
occupational epidemiology and the EMSU.

Dissemination of information on epidemiology both to and
from EMAS is achieved by collaboration with industry, Medical
Research Council Units, academic institutions and others with
whom EMAS collaborates in joint studies. It is EMAS policy to
encourage epidemiological investigation of occupational
hazards. In many cases EMAS, with its national organisation
and well-established links with industry and unions at local
level, is best equiped to take on the work.

Due to their disparate nature, no attempt is made here to
draw together different reports of accident epidemiology.
Details will be found in the annotated bibliography of a
number of studies which may be regarded as typical rather than
of comprehensive coverage ([78]-[89].

The remainder of this section will be devoted to briefly
describing several in-house EMAS conducted epidemiological
studies (reported in "Employment and Medical Advisory
Service. Health and Safety 1981-1982" (1984)). Although not
published formally, these studies provide interesting
epidemiological information in a number of areas.

- Asbestos Workers

The EMAS survey of workers in premises covered by the Asbestos
Regulations 1969 has continued with the aid of Institute of

Occupational Medicine in the interpretation of X-Ray materials. (Jacobson et al, 1983) [90]. The survey has been able to provide estimates of the prevelance of radiological abnormality in the survey population. A clear difference was demonstrated between workers exposed before the 1969 Regulations and those exposed after they came into effect. It is hoped that an analysis of the birth cohort mortality pattern and detailed tabulations of mesothelioma deaths will form the basis of a future publication.

- Lead Workers

There have been problems with the data from lead woorkers surveys although these have largely been resolved. EMAS have reported that further flagging and tracing of the population will be necessary before a final mortality analysis can be performed. A blood-lead computer file system is now in operation.

- Foundry Workers

Mortality data obtained from previous morbidity studies of foundry men are at present under analysis. As part of the investigation of an observed increased incidence of lung cancer in the community near a Scottish steel foundry, work on the mortality study set up in 1978 has proceeded.

- Acrylonitrile

A report on the mortality of 1,111 men to the end of 1978 who have worked on the polymerisation of acrylonitrile and spinning of acrylic fibre, between 1950 and 1968, was published in 1981 (Werner & Carter, 1981 [91]). The population was drawn from six factories in England, Wales, Northern Ireland and Scotland. In a group of men exposed to acrylonitrile for at lease one year, the total number of deaths was less than expected. A slight statistically insignificant excess of death from all cancer was found, arising mainly from cancer of the lung, stomach, colon and brain. The results are not conclusive and neither confirm nor confound suspicions that acrylonitrile is a human carcinogen. Taken with evidence from other studies however they indicate the need for more information on the U.K. population. This study is therefore being extended to cover workers first exposed at the same six factories in the period 1969 to 1978.

- Carpet Dust

A study of carpet backwinders was conducted to investigate the prevalence of respiratory symptoms and epistaxis in this population compared with a control group. A significant excess of certainrespiratory symptoms was found among the workforce exposed to wool or nylon dust and this has been reported in full by Allardice et al (1983) [92].

- Pentachlorophenol Production

Following the finding of two cases of non-Hodgkin's lymphoma arising in the subcutaneous tissue of two workers whose occupational history at a chemical company included a period of work in a PCP plant, a nominal roll of all persons identified from company records as having worked on this process was compiled and searched via the Cancer Registry for further cases. No further cases were uncovered

But, with the help of the personnel records, an expected number of cases of non-Hodgkin's lumphoma for this population was calculated. The population has now been flagged for mortality and cancer registration, at the expense of the company concerned. If further cases occur, they will be reported immediately.

- Carbon Black

The mortality study of workers exposed to carbon black fibre in five factories during the period 1947 to 1980 has been completed. These factories produced almost the whole U.K. output of carbon black (two of them are now closed), which is used principally in the rubber industry and in the manufacture of printing inks. A final report is being prepared for publication.

- Other Studies

The mortality study of workers potentially exposed to styrene in the course of its production and polymerisation is being completed by EMSU. Also, evidence of any possible long-term effects of styrene exposure will be sought in a study of workers sxposed to styrene during the laminating of glass.

Some field work has been carried out on the use of radio-immune hormone assay techniques in the biological surveillance of people who are involved in the manufacture of oral contraceptives. EMAS reports that the results suggest that these techniques may form a useful and practical method of assessing occupational absorption.

A prevalence study of lung function and respiratory symptoms in roadstone quarry workers has been carried out in the North East of England. The data are currently being analysed by EMSU.

A mortality follow-up of the population from thirty five cotton mills in South East Lancashire, which were the subject of a 1973 morbidity study, is currently being prepared.

5.6 Bibliography

48   POWELL, P.J., HALE, M., MARTIN, J. and SIMON, M.   "2000 Accidents": a shop floor study of their causes". Report No. 21 of the NIIP 1971. pp 189.

Still one of the most widely read and respected studies of occupational accidents, this report holds up well today still. Data were collected by on-site observers in four workshops, each examined for at least a year. Details of 2,367 accidents were collected. The study was oriented towards the application of knowledge of accidents to produce methods for their reduction, rather than being a theoretical analysis of accident behaviour was aimed at kapplying knowledge to prevent accidents rather than as a theoretical analysis of accident behaviour. Evidence was given to show the multiple nature of the factors affecting accidents. Although the study was published in 1971 it is still considered to be a major contribution to accident research in Britain, particularly due to its proposals for legislative pressure.

49   HEALTH AND SAFETY EXECUTIVE (HSE).   "Managing Safety" Occasional Paper No. 3 (0118834436).   1981.

50   BEAUMONT, P.B.   An analysis of the problem of industrial accidents in Britain.   Int. Jr. of Manpower, Jol. 1, No. 1, p 28-32   1980.

Examines inter-industry variations in accident rates for the manufacturing rates for the manufacturing sector in Britian, by looking at the role of job and worker characteristics in accident causation.

51   WARBURTON, R.M.   The factory inspectorate and its changing role.   Employee relations, Vol. 2, No. 4, p 6-11.   1980.

Considers the implications of HASAWA and the Robens Committee for the role of the factory inspectorate - the balance between enforcing and advising the encouragement of more participation by the workforce in safety matters, and the need for health and safety to be considered not only in the broader climate of social opinion but also of industrial relations.

52   HEALTH AND SAFETY EXECUTIVE (HSE)   "Employment Medical Advisory Service Report Health and Safety 1981 - 1982" London: HMSO. 1984 pp 44.

This report covers the activities and developments of the Health and Safety Executive Employment Medical Advisory Service for the years 1981 and 1982.   It is the latest report of this kind.   Interesting sections include 'hazards in particular industries', 'epidermeology', and 'work with disabled people'.   A large set of useful appendices is included.

53   GLENDON, A. and BOOTH, R.T.   Worker participation in occupational health and safety in Britain, Int. Labour Review, Vol. 121 No. 4 p 399-416.   1982.

They review the current modes and degree of worker participation in health and safety in UK.   They cover institutional forms of participation so that a national and company level and consider mechanisms of participation such as training and trades unions.

54   MCKINNON, R.   Occupational Health: Investing in commonsense, The Director, Feb, p 29-30 1982.

A very short paper which discusses setting up of Institute of Occupational Health and its immediate priorities.   These are to provide such assistance to companies as EMAS cannot, to conduct particular studies, and to work actively twoards improving the industrial environment.

55. McDONALD, J.C.   Four pillars of occupational health.
     B.M.J., _282_, 3rd January 1981, 83-83, 88.

     A succinct summary of the actions required to produce a
     successful, universal system of occupational health in
     this   country.   Recommendations   consider
     employer-employee relationships, provision of and
     training for universal basic services, and a national
     framework of epidemiological surveillance and research.

56. HSC.   "Occupational Health Services: the way ahead.
     London: HMSO.   1978.

57. THOMAS, H.F.   Some observations on occupational hygiene
     standards, Ann. Occup. Hygiene, Vol. 22, p 389-397, 1979.

     Examines the difficulties associated with scientific
     aspects of standard setting by comparing those produced
     by 5 different organisations, showing a marked variation
     in content.   The importance of technical and economic
     factors is also discussed.

58. HEALTH AND SAFETY COMMISSION "The Control of Major
     Hazards" Third report of the Advisory Committee in Major
     Hazards.   London: HMSO 1984 pp 66.

     This report reviews progress made following earlier
     reports in 1976 and 1979, particularly with respect to
     notification schemes, planning controls and hazard
     surveys.   This third report concentrates upon the need
     for control over potential major hazards, examining their
     risk,   recognition   and   assessment,   avoidance   and
     mitigation.   A particular concern of the report, and of
     the Commission, is the transport of dangerous substances,
     the subject of an extended appendix.

59. HEALTH AND SAFETY EXECUTIVE   "Guide to the Control of
     Industrial Major Accident Hazard - Regulations.   HSE
     Booklet HS (R) 21.   1984.

60. KETTLE, M. "Disabled people and accidents at work". J of Occup. Accidents, 6, p 277 - 293 1984.

This reports a study which compared the accident rates of disabled workers with those of able-bodied workers within a sample of companies based in the West Midlands.

61. TAYLOR, P.J. and BURRIDGE, J. "Trends in death, disablement and sickness absence in the British Post Office since 1891." British Journal of Industrial Medicine, Vol. 39, p1-10. 1981.

62. MACKAY, C.J. and BISHOP, C.M. "Occupational health of women at work" (In: [64]).
The article discusses the various stresses which work may impose on the physical and mental well-being of women at work. Particular aspects considerd are employment and health; physical health (anthropometric differences from males, muscular strength and endurance, safe loads, the reproductive systems, other features, etc.); and mental health and job design.

63 SHIMMIN, S. "Pressures on factory women: between the devil and the deep blue sea" (In: [64]).

It is argued that many working women are exposed to negative and opposing pressures; caught between the unremitting demands of home and family. Pressures are said to include financial necessity, the restricted job market open to mothers, their prime responsibility for child care, lack of leisure time, and the monotony at both work and home. Consequences in terms of physical and mental stresses and ill-health, and of self-image, are expanded upon.

64 Ergonomics. "Women at Work". Special issue of the journal Ergonomics, 27/5, May 1984. pp 143.

A special journal issue based upon a 1983 conference on women at work. Contributions consider all aspects of this, considering occupational health and safety in a wide as well as narrow sense, and examining particular areas of employment, as well as unemployment.

65   BONNEY, M.C. and YONG, Y.F. (eds) "Robot Safety." IFS (publications) Ltd. Bedford 1985.

Presents up to date account of practice and developments in robot safety, with safety standard and codes of practice providing the framework. The book has a wide range of articles under the five sections of legislation and standards, surveys and analyses, system design, implementation and methodology, systems components and case studies. It has contributions not only from the U.K. but also U.S.A., Sweden, Italy, W. Germany and Japan.

66.   PEARSON, G.N., "Robot System Safety Issues Best Considered in Design Phase," Occup. Health and Safety, Vol 53, No. 8, Sept, p38 - 42, 1984,

In addition to describing the types of industrial robot available and their potential hazards, Pearson stresses the importance considering safety factors at the earliest stage, namely, in the initial design phase.

67.   PERCIVAL, N. "Safety Aspects of Industrial Robots," Metal Construction, Vol. 16, No. 4, p 201-203, 1984.

Methods of identifying hazards of industrial robots by risk assessment are discussed, together with the identification of specific hazards from dust, fume and radiation to software programming errors. The legal position is described, together with a brief review of guidance literature available and same possible solutions to safety problems.

68. BELL, R. et al. "Assessment of industrial programmable electronic systems with particular reference to robotics safety ". London: Institute of Quality Assurance, 1983. In "Reliability 1983: Fourth National Reliability Conference" 6-8 July 1983. Proceedings vol. 1.

Describes the factory inspectorate viewpoint on the use of programmable Electronic Systems in industrial control. The need for the safety integrity assessment of many of these systems is identified, and an assessment methodology of wide application is described.

69. PEARCE, B.G. (ed) "Health Hazards of VDTs?" HUSAT Research Group, John Wiley and Sons, 1984. (235 pages).

This book aims to enable people to approach the question of the possible health hazards of working with VDUs in a more informed way. It presents 17 papers of variable quality covering aspects that are divided into three sections. The first of these examines the evidence for the alleged direct health hazards that might affect the safety of VDU users. The second considers indirect effects, such as stress or postural loads, of VDU work that might affect the health and comfort of operators. The final section considers various ways in which the quality of working life of VDU users might be improved.

70. HEALTH AND SAFETY EXECUTIVE, "Visual Display Units". HMSO, 1983 (29 pages).

This booklet is briefer than the 29 pages suggest, due to ample use of illustration. The first part discusses the possible health effects of VDUs, such as cataracts and facial dermatitis. The 2nd part is more extensive, covering the remaining aspects of work organisation, training, text format and workplace design. The appendices distinguish between the three main types of VDU task, and give a bibliography and sources of further information.

71. APEX, "New Technology: A Health and Safety Report"
     London 1985 (66 pages).

     This is a comprehensive publication with 9 chapters
     covering aspects of most concern regarding the current
     use of new technology among professional, executive,
     clerical and computer staff.   The topics covered range
     from lighting and ventilation, to stress and job design.
     In each chapter the topic in question is discussed in
     terms of recommendations from various sources, a
     statement of APEXpolicy regarding this matter, and
     relevant results of their 1981 and 1983-84 surveys are
     presented.   Appendices are presented on Health and
     Safety codes of practice, and a bibliography is presented

72. NRC, "Video displays, work and vision".   National
     Academy Press, Washington, D.C., 1983,   (272 pages).

     This study was not conducted in the U.K., but is relevant
     to the British situation.   It is one of the most
     comprehensive studies available, giving a particularly
     thorough treatment to visual aspects as the title
     suggests.   However it also deals well with job design
     and organizational variables, anthropometry and
     biomechanics, and research needs in the area.   Over 300
     references are provided.

73. HARRINGTON, J.M.   "Shiftwork and Health: A critical
     Review of the Literature."   Health and Safety Executive
     (EMAS), London: HMSO.   1978.

     This represents a world literature review dealing with
     about two hundred references.   A good evaluation of the
     work in the shiftwork field, clearly written, and which
     stands up well seven years later.   Mortality and effects
     on sickness absence, sleep, circadiam rhythms, accidents
     and particular diseases are discussed.

74. EUROPEAN FOUNDATION FOR THE IMPROVEMENT OF LIVING AND WORKING CONDITIONS. "Shiftwork and Accidents" Report EF/82/6/EN. Dublin: European Foundation 1982 pp 129.

75. HEALTH AND SAFETY EXECUTIVE (HSE) "The problem drinker at work". Occasional paper. London: HMSO, 1981.

76. HYMAN, J. and BEAUMONT, P.B. Personnel and welfare: the case of the problem drinker at work. Employee Relations, 17/1, 1985, 17-21.

   Discusses welfare in relation to this problem and specifically tackles alcohol referral policies and alcohol recovery programmes. Written largely from the perspective of the duties and role of the personal function.

77. HARRINGTON, M. Epidemiology: the answer to every health question? Health and Safety at Work, August 1981, 36-38.

   A cautionary but positive introduction to the use and misuse, value or otherwise of the science of epidemiology. Considers types of epidemiological study, measures of exposure and response, study options and the uses of epidemiology in occupational health.

78. DAVIS, P.R. and SHEPPARD, N.J. (1980) Pattern of accident distribution in the telecommunication industry. Br. J. of Indus. Med., 37, p 175-179.

   Analysis of accident records in the telecommunications industry covering 100,000 engineers over a 12-month period.

79. Ergonomics, (1983) Vol 26, No. 1, Slipping, Tripping and Falling Accidents.

This special issue of Ergonomics reported on the 1 day conference on slipping, tripping and falling organized jointly by the Medical Commission on Accident Prevention and the University of Surrey Robens Institute of Industrial and Environmental Health and Safety.

80. LLOYD, O. "Epidemiology: Industry, occupation and the chemical environment". Occup. Health, 1981 p124 - 133.

Discusses the need to look beyond the confines of the factory when investigating occupational health problems, taking examples from the chemical industry.

81. MANNING, D.P. and SHANNON, H.S. Slipping accidents causing low-back pain in a gearbox factory. Spine, Vol. 6, No. 1, Jan/Feb 1981, p 70-72.

An accident model was used to analyze data in terms of the first event in all reported accidents in a gearbox factory, and the data used to study the causes of lumbrosacral injuries.

82. STUBBS, D.A. and NICHOLSON, A.S. (1979 "Manual Handling and Back Injuries in the Construction Industry: An Investigation". Jr. of Occup. Accs., 2, (1979), p179-190.

This analysis of manual handling accidents showed employees in trades classified as involving heavy physical labour to be most at risk, and in all trades those under 30 years of age had higher injury rates than those in older age groups.

83. ANDERSON, D.M. "From accident report to design problems - a study of accidents on board ship". Ergonomics, 26/1, 1983, 43-50.

As part of a study of boarding and disembarking from ships, sponsored by the National Maritime Institute, an analysis was made of all shipboard accident reports. Over 3,000 accidents were analysed in total. Data are classified by month, location, repetition, fatalities etc.

84. JOHNSON, M.A.   "PSV accident survey" MIRA Report No. K52503.   Nuneaton.   1981 pp 122.

A survey was made of bus accidents in which personal injury or severe bus damage was the result.   Analyses are concerned with bus type and characteristics, passenger (casualty) positions, others involved. etc.

85. BRYSON, D.D.   "A positive approach to assessment of chemical hazards in agriculture".   Ergonomics, 25/1, 1982, 81-87.

The importance of epidemiological research in this area is stressed, particularly in view of the changing nature of the hazards.   Long-term chronic effects are now perhaps more of a problem than acute poisoning incidents.

86. FERGUSON, J.C., McNALLY, M.S. and BOOTH, R.F., "Accidental injuries among naval personnel by occupation duty status and pay grade".   Accident Analysis and Prevention, 17/1, 1985, 79-86.

During 1974-77 an analysis was made of accidental injury relative frequencies across 68 occupations in the Navy. Difference in accident rate with occupation and degree of responsibility were found.

87. OWEN, G.M. and HUNTER, A.G.M.   "A survey of tractor overturning accidents in the U.K.".   J. of Occupational Accidents, 5/3, 1983, 185 - 193.

An eight year survey period (1968 - 76) provided 560 accidents for analysis. Classification showed 55% tractor-related (i.e. safe limits exceeded), 26% driver related (errors of judgement), and 19% classed as miscellaneous. Those accidents involving overturning on slopes were further analysed and reported on in the same journal issue (pp 195-210).

88. NUSSEY, C. Studies of accidents leading to minor injuries in the U.K. coal mining industry. J. of Occupational Accidents, 2/4, 1980, 305-323.

Methods and results of such studies, referring to over 3-day absence accidents, are discussed. The report acts as a signpost to detailed reports of the studies.

89. REILLY, M.S.J. "The safety of UK Fishing vessels 1961-80." J. of Navigation, 37/1, 1984, 60-82.

Loss and casualty rates for deep-sea and inshore fishing vessels were analysed for a 20 year period, establishing arise in the loss rate in that time. Certain background factors are assessed as potential causes of such a rise.

90. JACOBSON, M., MILLER, B.G., and MUROCH, R.M. "A study of a sample of chest radiographs from the Health and Safety Executives survey of asbestos workers" Institute of Occupational Medicine Report No. TM/83/4.

91. WERNER J.B., and CARTER J.T. "Mortality of United Kingdom Acrylonitrile Polymerisation Workers." in British Journal of Industrial Medicine Vol. 38, p 247-253, 1981.

92. ALLARDICE, J.T., CLARKE E.C. and JONES R.D. "A study of the prevalence of epistaxis and respiratory symptoms in carpet backwinders" in Journal of the Society of Occupational Medicine Vol. 33, p 36-41, 1983.

CHAPTER 6

OVERALL EVALUATION

This chapter provides a summary review of the U.K.'s approach to occupational accidents and diseases. In doing this it will be necessary to generalise, and rely upon an overview drawn from the variety of areas covered in this report.

The 1974 Health and Safety at Work Act (HASAWA) and its objectives may be regarded as representative of the U.K. approach towards the health, safety and welfare of people at work. The Robens report, then the HASAWA and the proliferation of regulations and recommendations emanating from the latter represents the current U.K. philosophy towards occupational accidents and diseases. In other words, the key to U.K. occupational safety and health is the legislation that governs work activities in general.

The premise that 'preventative' legal requirements are an efficient and successful way in which health and safety matters can be dealt with is fundamental in understanding the U.K. system. The belief that conditions at work can be improved via statutory instruments and the state agencies (the Health and Safety Commission, and the Health and Safety Executive) has been promoted.

In recent years policy-making by the HSC and HSE has been affected greatly by large reductions in their available resources. It now appears to be common practice to adopt a cost/benefit approach when dealing with such issues as research, staffing, and administration generally [2]. The HSE, the operations arm of the HASAWA, has been the victim of cuts in budgets, and this has been attributed to the 'current economic recession'.

Ridley (1983) [93] has claimed that the "health and safety laws of the UK are the most complex and comprehensive of all employment laws", in his thorough and authoritative coverage of the situation in Great Britain. This is undoubtedly the case, and would appear to be the result of the inherited legal system. The review by Ridley deals with the gamut of health and safety topics considered in the UK.

The overall trends in UK employment such as moves from the traditional industries to the service industries, together with the impact of the information technology revolution, the rather general decline of British manufacturing industry, and increased unemployment, has been reflected in the UK health and safety policies. Similarly, public concern over certain issues has prompted policy moves; for example, asbestosis regulations.

In 1984, Singleton [94] looked at the trends within accident research in Europe. His impressions were that future work in the UK and abroad is more likely to concentrate on eppidemiological approaches to the monitoring of the vast amounts of new chemicals. The beginning of a trend away from accident research towards research into occupational diseases has been witnessed in the UK.

With respect to the 1980's the occupational health and safety field has seen a number of major changes. On the one hand, great progress has been made in tackling such problems as the control of asbestos at work, occupational deafness and a number of hygiene-related topics (e.g. carcinogenic substances). On the other hand, however, abolition of many industrial injury benefits (e.g. death benefit and injury benefit) has had far-reaching implications. Many would argue that such changes have proved a set-back to the aims of the HASAWA. It should be appreciated that 'simplification' of the state benefit schemes (compensation) has meant upheaval for reporting and notification of occupational accidents and diseases, indeed has created an unacceptable situation of accident and disease data collection and presentation.

State-governed occupational health services remain a dream of those within the field, and employers' resistance to increased levels of worker protection and burgeoning legislation have been criticised. Similarly, delays in the implementation of advisory bodies' recommendations have been under attack.

As far as the courts are concerned, the attitude of the past decade has been relatively sympathetic to the worker disabled as a result of work-related accidents and diseases. Recent civil court actions for compensation have been fairly successful (e.g. cases of occupational deafness, or more generally employer negligence). Meanwhile the industrial injuries benefits scheme changes have not been particularly kind to the 'victims' of occupational diseases or accidents.

When examining the state of reporting and notification of accidents/diseases in the U.K. it is all too apparent that the position is unstable. From the employers' point of view, the introduction of a new reporting system in 1980 followed by I.I.B.S. alterations and the consequent 1983 proposed revision of the Regulations is not satisfactory. At present, a situation exists whereby the 1980 NADOR are still effective yet information which was provided by the DHSS is now lost. Obviously, another set of regulations will be devised to cover the appalling loss of data. The introduction of new reporting regulations is planned for January, 1986.

Naturally, the reporting changes have affected statistical information. The break in 1981, when the NADOR came into effect, has meant that figures cannot be meaningfully compared across this break. Of course, another change in the notification system will produce a similar deficiency in the U.K. health and safety statistics, which in any case are delayed at present.

Recently, the HSC approach to research activities has been somewhat rigidly specified. The areas covered fall into the broad classes of analytical methods for the identification of harmful substances; the monitoring of dust, fumes, and fibres; explosives and reactive chemicals investigation; and gas and vapour research. Again, budget reductions have affected HSE research initiatives. Perhaps the HSE's work on issues such as asbestos and major hazards represent the most successful projects undertaken.

To summarise the achievements (or otherwise) made since the HASAWA 1974 became fully operative [2]:

a) The institutions for co-operation in standard setting between the HSE and major industries are in place. A formidable apparatus of advisory committees is functioning well;

b) The HSE has gained in cohesion. Its technological and information capacity has been consolidated and has grown considerably. The inspectorates have learned to work together and new units drawn from various parts of the organisation have been formed;

c) The new tools for enforcement provided by the HASAWA, particularly improvement and prohibition notices, have been accepted within industry, and a new pattern of regulatory provisions (involving regulations, codes of practice and guidance material) has been established;

d) The number of industrial accidents (up to 1980 figures) have declined considerably by rather more than the decline in manufacturing employment can explain itself.

The main prescription of a steady increase in concern with safety and health in industry (Robens [1]) has, with some setbacks due to the recession, been fulfilled. However;

a) the reform of safety law (section 1 of the HASAWA) has only partially been accomplished. Major complexes of safety law such as maritime transport and offshore oil exploration require adjustments;

b) though procedures for consultation have improved considerably since the pre-HASAWA era the making of regulations is still a slow and usually painstaking process. Delays are attributable not only to the need to secure commitment but frequently also now to delays arising at international level;

c) Sources of information for 'traditional' accidents and particularly for ill-health as a consequence of work are incomplete and unsatisfactory;

d) occupational health provision in industry has not proceded at the pace originally hoped and expected;

e) the role of insurance in motivating accident prevention remains under-developed.

f) safety representatives and committees have established themselves as a significant influence in many enterprises. There is clearly scope for the further development of their role, and for a greater input to standards of health and safety at the workplace.

To conclude, the extensive health and safety field of occupational accidents and diseases has seen progress, however slow it may be. Over large areas of industry, particularly in the more traditional areas, changes in detailed legislation, methods and conditions of enforcement have probably been much slower than was ever envisaged. In the industrial areas which are newer, advisory institutions have been created; the HSE has developed considerably its scientific and technological facilities.

The occupational health and safety situation in Great Britain, over a decade after the revolutionary HASAWA, is one which still requires increased attention and increased resources. The changing nature of UK society, (for example, trends away from traditional industries) together with recent innovations (for example, new chemical hazards) has meant a change in emphasis with regard to research. Some areas, such as reporting and notification of accidents, collation and analysis of national statistics, compensation and liability legislation, indicate great room for improvement.

BIBLIOGRAPHY

93. RIDLEY, J. Safety at work. London: Butterworths 1983 pp 707.

A collection of contemporary papers from several leading authorities. Areas covered include the law (safety, industrial relations, contract, liability and compensation); safety management (techniques, reporting); behavioural science (individual, society); health and hygiene (diseases, radiation, noise and vibration, lighting, climate, ergonomics); and general science.

94. SINGLETON, W.T. Future trends in accident research in European countries, J. of Occ. Accidents, 6, 1984, 3-12.

Discusses future changes in trends of accident research, such as increased use of cost/benefit terms in assessment, increased monitoring for hazards, and a switch in emphasis from accidents to occupational diseases.

REFERENCES

1. ROBENS REPORT. "Report of the Committee on Safety and Health at Work, 1970 - 72". Cmnd. 5034. London: HMSO, 1972.

2. HEALTH AND SAFETY COMMISSION. "Plan of work 1985/86 and onwards". London: HMSO 1985. 44pp.

3. KINNERSLY, P. "The hazards of work: how to fight them" London: Pluto press 1973 394pp.

4. HEALTH AND SAFETY EXECUTIVE (HSE) "The notification of accidents and dangerous occurrences." (NADOR) Health and Safety series booklet HS(R)5. London: Her Majesty's Stationery Office (HMSO). 1980. pp43.

5. HEALTH AND SAFETY COMMISSION (HSC) "Proposals for revised arrangements for reporting accidents, ill-health, and dangerous occurrences at work." Consultative document. London: HMSO. 1983. pp24.

6. OCCUPATIONAL SAFETY & HEALTH, "New arrangements for reporting workplace accidents and ill health." Sept. 1985, p2.

7. ADAMS, N.L. and HARTWELL, N.M. "Accident-reporting systems: a basic problem area in industrial society." J. Occupational Psychology, 50, 1977, 285-298.

8. FANNING, D. "The compilation and use of accident statistics in the British Steel Corporation." B.S.C. - Sheffield Division, Sept. 1977. pp13.

9. KLETZ, T.A. "Accident data: the need for a new look at the sort of data that are collected and analysed". J. of Occup. Accidents, 1, p. 95-105, 1976.

10. SHANNON, H.S. and MANNING D.P. "A note on reported accident rates". J. of Occup. Accidents, 2, pp245-253, 1979.

11. HEALTH AND SAFETY EXECUTIVE (HSE) "Health and Safety Statistics 1980." A publication of the Government Statistical Service. London: HMSO. 1983. pp63.

12. HEALTH AND SAFETY EXECUTIVE (HSE) "Manufacturing and Services Industries 1983 report." London: HMSO. 1984. pp80.

13. HEALTH AND SAFETY COMMISSION (HSC) "Health and Safety Commission Report 1983-1984." London: HMSO. 1984. pp43.

14. DEPARTMENT OF HEALTH AND SOCIAL SECURITY (D.H.S.S.) "Social Security Act 1975 - Reform of the Industrial Injuries Scheme" Cmnd P042. London: H.M.S.O. November 1981. 30 pp.

15. ROWLAND, M. "The Industrial Injuries Benefits Scheme." Law and practice guide no. 6. London: Legal Action Group (LAG). July 1983. 122 pp.

16. DEPARTMENT OF HEALTH AND SOCIAL SECURITY (D.H.S.S.) "Injured at work, a guide to cash benefits." (FB. 15/Nov 84); "Disablement benefit and increases" (NI.196/April 83); "Social security rates and earnings rules" (NI.196/Nov 84); "Industrial death benefits - for widows and other dependants" (Nl.10/Mar 83); "Prescribed industrial diseases (Nl. 2/Dec 84). London: H.M.S.O.

17. MUNKMAN, J. "Employers Liability at Common Law." Ninth edition. London: Butterworths. 1979. 653 pp.

18. ROYAL COMMISSION ON CIVIL LIABILITY AND COMPENSATION FOR PERSONAL INJURY. Chairman: Lord Pearson. Volumes 1-3. Cmnd 7054. London: H.M.S.O. 1978.

19. COLLINSON, J.M. (1979) The Pearson report - compromise step or towards effective and just compensation for Brit disability? J. of Indust. Med. 36, 263-275.

20. SOCRATES, E. (1981) "Employer's Compensation Schemes". Occupational Safety and Health, March 26-27.

21. WHINCUP, M.   Compensation for accidents, Occ. Health, p205 May, 211, 1978 (7 pages).

22. ATIYAH, P.S. "Accidents, Compensation and the Law." Third edition.   London: Weidenfeld and Nicolson.   1980. 695 pp.

23. BARRET, B. (1981) "Employers' liability for work related ill-health".   Indust. Law J. Vol 10, 101-112.

24. WHINCUP, M. (1980) "Compensation for negligence". Occupational Health, April 1980. p.175-183.
25. WILSON, S.R."Occupational diseases" Ind. Law J.,II 141-145 1982
26. DEPARTMENT OF HEALTH AND SOCIAL SECURITY (DHSS) "Industrial injuries - INDUSTRIAL DEATH BENEFIT, for widows and other dependants." NI 10/Mar '83. London: HMSO. 1983 pp7.

27. HEALTH AND SAFETY EXECUTIVE (HSE).   "Fatal accidents in construction 1978". HM Factory Inspectorate Report.   London: HMSO, 1981 pp16.

28. HSE "Construction.   Health and Safety 1981-82" London: HMSO. 1983.   pp87.

29. MANNING, D. Slips and Falls.   Occupational Safety and Health.   July, 15-19, 1981 (5 pp).

30. HSE "Preventing falls to window cleaners." IND(S)4(L) M40 S/84; and"Working as fragile roofs" IND (G) 21 (L). Published by the HSE 1984.

31. HSE "Roofwork - prevention of falls." Guidance note GS10.   London: HMSO. 1983.

32. DEPARTMENT OF EMPLOYMENT (D.E.). "Code of Practice for reducing the exposure of employed persons to Noise." Her Majesty's Stationery Office (HMSO): London. 1972. 33pp

33. HEALTH AND SAFETY COMMISSION (H.S.C.). "Protection of hearing at work". HSC Consultative Document. London: HMSO. July 1981.

34. COMMISSION FOR THE EUROPEAN COMMUNITIES. "Amended proposal for a draft directive on noise". O.J.C. 214/84. 1984.

35. TEMPEST, W. Noise exposure and hearing loss. Annals of Occupational Hygiene, 21, 51-56, 1978 (6 pp)

35a ACTON, W.I. Can noise cause accidents? Occupational Safety and Health September, 14-16. 1982 (3pp).

36. DEPARTMENT OF HEALTH AND SOCIAL SECURITY (DHSS). "Occupational deafness. New rules - more people are now eligible for benefit." Leaflet NI.207/Mar 84. (Replaces edition of Oct 83.) London: HMSO.

37. DEPARTMENT OF HEALTH AND SOCIAL SECURITY (DHSS) "Prescribed Industrial Diseases." NI 2/Dec 1984. London: HMSO. 1984. pp11.

38. ACTON, W.I. and GRIME R.P. Noise and hearing loss compensation. Am. Occup. Hyg. Vol 23, pp205-215, 1980.

39. DEPARTMENT OF HEALTH AND SOCIAL SECURITY (DHSS). "Report on Occupational Deafness." Cmnd 8749. November 1982. London: HMSO.

40. HEALTH AND SAFETY EXECUTIVE (HSE). "100 practical applications of noise reduction methods." London: Her Majesty's Stationery Office (HMSO). 1983. 112pp.

41. BURNS, W. and ROBINSON, D.W. "Hearing and Noise in Industry". Department of Health and Social Security (DHSS). London: HMSO. 1970. 241pp.

42. HEALTH AND SAFETY COMMISSION (HSC) "Control of Asbestos at Work." Draft Regulations and Draft Code of Practice. Consultative Document. London: Her Majesty's Stationery Office. 1984. pp65.

43. HEALTH AND SAFETY EXECUTIVE (HSE) "A guide to the Asbestos (Licensing) Regulations 1983." Health and Safety Series booklet HS(R)19. London: HMSO. 1984. pp27.

44. HEALTH AND SAFETY COMMISSION (HSC) "Asbestos," Volume 1: Final Report of the Advisory Committee. Volume 2: - papers commissioned by the Committee." London: HMSO. 1979. Vol 1 pp100; Vol 2 pp103.

45. DEPARTMENT OF HEALTH AND SOCIAL SECURITY (DHSS) "Industrial injuries paid for Pneumonconiosis and Byssinosis." NI3/Sept '82. London: HMSO. 1983 S.

46. Russell, J. R. "Asbestos - a failure?" In: Essays to commemorate 150 years of health and safety inspection: Her Majesty's Inspectors of Factories 1933-1983. HSC, 37-39, 1983.

47. BARON, P. et al. " A summary of asbestos fibre counting experience in seven countries." Annals of Occupational Hygiene, 20, 321-332. 1977.

48. POWELL, P.J., HALE, M., MARTIN, J. and SIMON, M. "2000 Accidents: a shop floor study of their courses". Report No. 21 of the NIIP. 1971. pp 189.

49. HEALTH AND SAFETY EXECUTIVE (HSE). "Managing Safety" Occasional Paper No. 3 (0118834436). 1981.

50. BEAUMONT, P.B. " An analysis of the problem of industrial accidents in Britain." Int. Jr. of Manpower, Vol. 1, No. 1, p 28-32. 1980.

51. WARBURTON, R.M.   "The factory inspectorate and its changing role."   Employee Relations, Vol. 2, No. 4, p 6-11.   1980.

52. HEALTH AND SAFETY EXECUTIVE (HSE)   "Employment Medical Advisory Service Report Health and Safety 1981 - 1982" London: HMSO. 1984 pp 44.

53. GLENDON, A. and BOOTH, R.T. "Worker participation in occupational health and safety in Britain". Int. Labour Review, Vol. 121 No. 4, p399-416.   1982.

54. McKINNON, R.   "Occupational Health: Investing in commonsense". The Director, Feb. 1982, p 29-30.

55. McDONALD, J.C. "Four pillars of occupational health." B.M.J., 282, 3rd January 1981, 83-88.

56. HSC.   "Occupational Health Services: the way ahead." London: HMSO.   1978.

57. THOMAS, H.F.   "Some observations on occupational hygiene standards." Ann. Occup. Hygiene, Vol. 22, p389-397, 1979.

58. HEALTH AND SAFETY COMMISSION "The Control of Major Hazards." Third Report of the Advisory Committee on Major Hazards.   London: HMSO 1984 pp 66.

59. HEALTH AND SAFETY EXECUTIVE   "Guide to the Control of Industrial Major Accident Hazard - Regulations." HSE Booklet HS (R) 21.   1984.

60. KETTLE, M. "Disabled people and accidents at work." Jrnl. of Occup. Accidents, 6, 1984. pp277-293.

61. TAYLOR, P.J. and BURRIDGE, J.   "Trends in death, disablement and sickness absence in the British Post Office since 1891." British Journal of Industrial Medicine, Vol. 39, p1-10.   1981.

62. MACKAY, C.J. and BISHOP, C.M.   "Occupational health of women at work" (In: [64]).

63. SHIMMIN, S.   "Pressures on factory women: between the devil and the deep blue sea" (In: [64]).

64. Ergonomics.   "Women at Work".   special issue of the journal Ergonomics, 27/5, May 1984. pp 143.

65. BONNEY, M.C. and YONG, Y.F. (eds) Robot Safety.   IFS (Publications) Ltd. Bedford 1985.

66. PEARSON, G.N.   Robot System Safety Issues Best Considered in Design Phase, Occup. Health and Safety, Vol 53, No. 8, Sept, p38 - 42, 1984, (5 pages).

67. PERCIVAL, N.   Safety Aspects of Industrial Robots, Metal Construction, Vol. 16, No. 4, p 201-203, 1984, (3 pages).

68. BELL, R. et al.   Assessment of Industrial programmable Electronic Systems with particular reference to robotics safety., London, Institute of Quality Assurance, 1983. In "Reliability 1983: fourth national reliability conference, 6-8 July 1983: proceedings" vol. 1.

69. PEARCE, B.G. (ed) Health Hazards of VDTs ?   HUSAT Research Group, John Wiley and Sons, 1984.   (235 pages).

70. HEALTH AND SAFETY EXECUTIVE, Visual Display Units, HMSD, 1983 (29 pages).

71. APEX New Technology: A Health and Safety Report, 1985 (66 pages).

72.   NRC Video displays, work and vision.   National Academy
      Press, Washington, D.C., 1983, (272 pages).

73.   HARRINGTON, J.M.   "Shiftwork and Health: A critical
      Review of the Literature."   Health and Safety Executive
      (EMAS), London: HMSO.   1978.

74.   EUROPEAN FOUNDATION FOR THE IMPROVEMENT OF LIVING AND
      WORKING CONDITIONS.   "Shiftwork and Accidents" Report
      EF/82/6/EN.   Dublin: European Foundation 1982 pp 129.

75.   HEALTH AND SAFETY EXECUTIVE (HSE) "The problem drinker at
      work".   Occasional paper.   London: HMSO, 1981.

76.   HYMAN, J. and BEAUMONT, P.B.   Personnel and welfare:
      the case of the problem drinker at work.   Employee
      Relations, 17/1, 1985, 17-21.

77.   HARRINGTON, M. Epidemiology: the answer to every health
      question?   Health and Safety at Work, August 1981,
      36-38.

78.   DAVIS, P.R. and SHEPPARD, N.J. (1980)   Pattern of
      accident distribution in the telecommunication industry.
      Br. J. of Indus. Med., 37, p 175-179.

79.   Ergonomics, (1983) Vol 26, No. 1, January Slipping,
      Tripping and Falling Accidents.

80.   LLOYD, O.   Epidemiology: Industry, Occupation and the
      Chemical Environment, Occup. Health, 1981, p124 - 133.

81.   MANNING, D.P. and SHANNON, H.S. Slipping Accidents
      causing low-back pain in a gearbox factory, Spine,
      Vol. 6, No. 1, Jan/Feb 1981, p 70-72.

82.   STUBBS, D.A. and NICHOLSON, A.S.   "Manual Handling and
      Back Injuries in the Construction Industry: An
      Investigation".   Jr. of Occup. Accs., 2, (1979),
      p179-190.

83. ANDERSON, D.M. "From accident report to design problems - a study of accidents on board ship". Ergonomics, 26/1, 1983, 43-50.

84. JOHNSON, M.A. "PSV accident survey" MIRA Report No. K52503. Nuneaton. 1981 pp 122.

85. BRYSON, D.D. "A positive approach to assessment of chemical hazards in agriculture". Ergonomics, 25/1, 1982, 81-87.

86. FERGUSON, J.C., McNALLY, M.S. and BOOTH, R.F., "Accidental injuries among naval personnel by occupation duty status and pay grade". Accident Analysis and Prevention, 17/1, 1985, 79-86.

87. OWEN, G.M. and HUNTER, A.G.M. "A survey of tractor overtiming accidents in the U.K.". J. of Occupational Accidents, 5/3, 1983, 185 - 193.

88. NUSSEY, C. Studies of accidents leading to minor injuries in the U.K. coal mining industry. J. of Occupational Accidents, 2/4, 1980, 305-323.

89. REILLY, M.S.J. "The safety of UK Fishing vessels 1961-80." J. of Navigation, 37/1, 1984, 60-82.

90. JACOBSON, M., MILLER, B.G., and MUROCH, R.M. "A study of a sample of chest radiographs from the Health and Safety Executive's survey of asbestos workers" Institute of Occupational Medicine Report No. TM/83/4.

91. WERNER J.B., and CARTER J.T. "Mortality of United Kingdom Acrylonitrile Polymerisation Workers." British Journal of Industrial Medicine Vol. 38, p 247-253, 1981.

92. ALLARDICE, J.T., CLARKE E.C. and JONES R.D. "A study of the prevalence of epistaxis and respiratory symptoms in carpet backwinders." Journal of the Society of Occupational Medicine Vol. 33, p 36-41, 1983.

93. RIDLEY, J. Safety at work.   London: Butterworths 1983
     pp 07.

94. SINGLETON, W.T.   Future trends in Accident Research in
     European Countries, J. of Occ. Accidents, 6, 1984, 3-12.

British Occupational Hygiene Society, 101
Chichester, 5

SUBJECT INDEX

APPENDIX I

OUTLINE OF OCCUPATIONAL ACCIDENT AND DISEASE REPORTING CRITERIA IN
THE UK

Present Legal Situation

As from January 1981 (under the Notification of Accidents and
Dangerous Occurrences Regulations (1980)), the notification and
reporting of accidents and incidents arising out of or in connection
with work, has been based upon four distinct classes of incident.
These are:

a) Fatal accidents (accidents resulting in death);

b) Major injury accidents, defined as
   - fracture of the skull, spine or pelvis
   - fracture of any bone in the arm (other than a bone in the
     wrist or hand) or leg (other than a bone in the ankle or
     foot);
   - amputation of a hand or foot;
   - the loss of sight of an eye; or
   - any other injury which results in the person being admitted
     to hospital for more than 24 hours as an in-patient, unless
     that person is detained for observation only.

c) Other accidents - accidents which are neither fatal nor major,
   originally known as "3-day accidents", and which result in an
   incapacity for work of more than 3 days, excluding rest days and
   the day of the accident, where industrial injury benefit is
   claimed.

d) Dangerous occurrences - a class of incidents listed in the
   Regulations (Schedule 1.1). Representative examples include
   collapse or part collapse of a scaffold, ignition or explosion
   of explosives, electric shock or burns, failure of rope haulage
   system, uncontrolled release of potentially harmful substances.

The action required by the employer (or responsible person) under
the Notification of Accidents and Dangerous Occurrences Regulations
(1980) is as follows:

(a) Fatal accidents, major injury accidents and dangerous occurrences (whether or not accompanied by injury):

1. Notify the local office of the enforcing authority as soon as reasonably practicable by telephone.

2. Confirm the notification in writing within seven days (using form F2508).

3. Keep a copy of the form (F2508) for record purposes and make it available to the enforcing authority or safety representative if required.

(b) Other accidents (ie those resulting in incapacity for more than 3 days where injured employee claims industrial injury benefit):

1. Await receipt of form B176 from the Department of Health and Social Security (DHSS).

2. On receipt of above complete and return both copies to DHSS.

3. Keep a copy of form B176 for record purposes and make available to the enforcing authority or safety representative if required.

There are several exemptions from the Notification of Accidents and Dangerous Occurences Regulations (1980). These are generally areas in which certain existing provisions are considered adequate and have therefore been retained. The exemptions can be summarised as -

i) certain accidents involving explosives - those arising from poisonous agricultural substances, those occurring in railway or merchant shipping industries, at nuclear installations, and in the field of civil aviation;

ii) medical and military accidents - those occurring to patients undergoing treatment, accidents to regular servicemen, reserve and visiting forces when on duty;

iii) road traffic accidents;

iv) road traffic accidents when engaged in work or alongside a road as a result of work;

v) those involved in work experience schemes (as in Education (Work Experience) Act 1973).

For iv) and v) above, should a person suffer a fatal or major accident then it will be directly reportable to the enforcing authority.

Situation in Practice

As reported in Chapter 2, the industrial injuries benefit scheme was changed in 1983 with the resulting loss of approximately 80 per cent of the information received by the Health and Safety Executive (HSE) via the DHSS (other accidents). Therefore, in 1983 the Health and Safety Commission (HSC) put forward proposals for a re-arranged reporting and notification scheme. However, the present situation is that the 1980 Notification of Accidents and Dangerous Occurrences Regulations which remain effective until new regulations are drawn up. Obviously, this change in the benefits scheme has had a deleterious effect upon the statistical data collection, and also leaves employers unclear as to reporting of 3-day accidents which were reportable prior to 1981.

New Proposals

The document "Proposals for revised arrangements for reporting accidents, ill-health and dangerous occurrence at work" (1983) outlines the proposed changes in reporting regulations. A provisional date for such regulations has been set as January 1986.

The proposals, which remain at the discussion level, involve a return to the reporting system which operated prior to 1981. 'Lost-time' accidents would be re-introduced, and work-related chronic ill-health and occupational diseases will become reportable. The proposed system aims to encompass all reportable information relating to ill-health and incidents, based upon the 1980 Notification of Accidents and Dangerous Occurrences Regulations.

APPENDIX 2

UK OCCUPATIONAL ACCIDENT AND DISEASE DATA FOR 1982

The following tables present the available (published) health and
safety statistics for 1982. As was previously stated (Chapter 2)
the full set of statistics for the year 1982 are currently being
collated by the Health and Safety Executive (HSE) and are due for
publication around June 1985.

It has, therefore, been necessary to rely upon the statistics which
have appeared in official publications by the HSC/HSE. In this
case, the major source of statistics has been the "Health and Safety
Commission 1983-1984 Report," the most recent annual report of this
kind. Delays in compilation and publication of the complete 1982
statistics has been attibuted to the alterations in the industrial
injuries benefits scheme, and the consequent lack of information
from the Department of Health and Social Security. (DHSS).

As a result of the Notification of Accidents and Dangerous
Occurrences Regulations (1980) there is a break in the continuity of
the statistics; that is the data for 1981 onwards are not directly
comparable with those of earlier years. Another break will occur
because of alterations in the DHSS benefits and the impact on injury
statistics for 1983 and thereafter.

Tables

(A) Deaths from occupational diseases resulting in awards of
industrial death benefit etc. by scheme 1978-1982.

(B) Dangerous Occurrences reported to enforcement authorities by
type, 1982.

(C) Injuries to employees reportable to enforcement authorities by
broad industrial analysis and severity of injury, 1982.

(D) Injuries to employees and others reported to HSC/HSE enforcement
authorities 1982.

A) DEATHS FROM OCCUPATIONAL DISEASES RESULTING IN AWARDS OF INDUSTRIAL DEATH BENEFIT etc. BY SCHEME 1978-1982.

	1978	1979	1980	1981	1982
Industrial injuries scheme death benefit awards:					
(i) pneumoconiosis - (including asbestosis)	(P) 589	(P) 609	(P) 588	(P) 539	(P) 552
(ii) other prescribed diseases	(P) 147	(P) 169	(P) 175	(P) 217	(P) 219
Certification that death was due to pneumoconiosis (Workman's compensation scheme)	54	60	66	68	48
Pneumoconiosis, byssinosis + miscellaneous diseases benefit scheme death benefit awards.	81	77	81	50	54
Total all schemes	871	915	910	874	873

(P) = Provisional

Source: DHSS - Department of Health and Social Security

B) <u>DANGEROUS OCCURRENCES REPORTED TO ENFORCEMENT AUTHORITIES BY TYPE, 1982</u>

Code No.	Type of dangerous occurrence (code description)	No. reported
	Dangerous occurrences to be notifiable in relation to any place of work -	
01	Failure, collapse or overturning of lifting machinery...	704
02	Explosion, collapse or bursting of any closed vessel...	277
03	Electrical fault causing fire or explosion...	153
04	Explosion or fire due to ignition of process materials, waste or finished products	340
05	Uncontrolled release or escape of highly flammable liquids.	106
06	Collapse or part collapse of scaffold.	38
07	Collapse or partial collapse at any building or structure under construction.	29
08	Uncontrolled release or escape of potentially harmful substance.	670
09	Personal exposure to, or contact with, a harmful substance, or lack of oxygen.	147
10	Ill-health resulting from exposure to isolated pathogens or infected material.	13
11	Ignition of explosion of explosives	86
12	Failure or collapse of a lifted freight container or part thereof.	10
13	Bursting, explosion or collapse of a pipe-line or any part thereof or the ignition of anything in a pipe-line.	97
14	Overturning or serious damage to the tank while conveying prescribed hazardous substance.	28
	Dangerous occurrences which are notifiable in relation to mines:	
21	Ignition of gas or dust below ground	9
22	Accidental gas ignition on the surface	10
23	Outbreaks of fire below ground	65

Code No.	Type of dangerous occurrence (code description)	No. reported
24	Withdrawal of men owing to smoke	16
25	Fires on the surface	2
26	Outbursts	2
27	Breakage of man-carrying ropes, etc. in shaft staple pits and unwalkable outlets	4
28	Breakage of man-carrying ropes, etc. below ground	19
29	Overwinds	4
30	Breakdown of ventilating apparatus	140
31	Collapse of certain surface buildings or structures	2
32	Failure of breathing apparatus, etc.	–
33	First-aid or medical treatment arising out of use of breathing apparatus, etc.	1
34	Electric shock or burns	20
35	Injuries from blasting materials or devices	9
36	Use of apparatus in pursuance of the Mines (Emergency Egress) Regulations 1973	7
37	Inrushes of gas from old workings	2
38	Inrushes of water, etc.	7
39	Unstable or potentially unstable waste heaps or settling ponds.	1
	Dangerous occurrences which are notifiable in relation to quarries	
51	Collapse of load-bearing structure	3
52	Sinking or overturning of waterborne craft of hovercraft.	–
53	Injuries from blasting materials or devices	3
54	Substance projected beyond quarry boundaries by blasting operations	24
55	Electric shock or burns	6
56	Unstable or potentially unstable tip	12

Code No.	Type of dangerous occurrence (code description)	No. reported
	Dangerous occurrences which are notifiable in relation to railways:	
61	Failure of locomotive	1
62	Failure of railway vehicle	-
63	Failure of rope haulage system	2
64	Failure of permanent way or formation	-
65	Trains or vehicles striking obstruction on line	-
66	Collision, derailment or trans becoming divided	1
67	Failure of level crossing equipment or trains (unauthorised) running onto level crossings	-
68	Other not elsewhere classified	82
	Total:	3152

Source: HSC Report 1983-84

(C)   INJURIES TO EMPLOYEES, REPORTABLE TO
       ENFORCEMENT AUTHORITIES: BY SEVERITY
       OF INJURY 1982 (REVISED) AND
       BROAD INDUSTRIAL ANALYSIS

Order No.	Standard Industrial Classification (SIC)	Fatal Injuries	Major Injuries	Fatal and Major (no)	Injur (rate per 100,0
i	Agriculture, forestry, fishing	27	147	174	49.
ii	Mining and Quarrying	73	1059	1132	349.
iii	Food, drink, tobacco	10	530	540	89.
iv	Coal & petroleum products	3	50	53	211.
v	Chemicals & allied industries	6	332	338	88.
vi	Metal manufacture	27	470	497	171.
vii	Mechanical engineering	18	457	475	66.
viii	Instrument engineering	–	31	31	23.
ix	Electrical engineering	8	180	188	29.
x	Shipbuilding and Marine eng.	8	148	156	112.
xi	Vehicles	5	267	272	49.
xii	Metal goods not elsewhere specified	10	396	406	96.
xiii	Textiles	6	198	204	68.
xiv	Leather, leather goods, fur	–	26	26	91.
xv	Clothing and footwear	1	35	36	14.
xvi	Bricks, pottery, glass, cement	11	229	240	118.
xvii	Timber, furniture, etc.	6	290	296	145.
xviii	Paper, printing, publishing	6	269	275	56.
xix	Other manufacturing industries	2	145	147	62.
	Total all manufacturing industries	127	4053	4180	74.
xx	Construction	100	1950	2050	204.
xxi	Gas, electricity, water	13	169	182	55.
xxii	Transport, communication	52	523	575	42.
xxiii	Distribution trades	10	219	229	8.
xxiv	Insurance, banking, finance.	3	9	12	0.
xxv	Professional and scientific services	4	1103	1107	30.
xxvi	Miscellaneous services	16	516	532	21
xxvii	Public administration and defence	14	1051	1065	71
	Unclassified (†)	32	1491	1523	

Total all injuries   471   12290   12761   62.2

(† = mainly injuries reported to local authorities, approx

400 returns.

Source: H.S.C. (1983-84 report).

D) <u>INJURIES TO EMPLOYEES AND OTHERS REPORTED TO HSC/HSE ENFORCEMENT</u>
   <u>AUTHORITIES, 1982.</u>
   (Summary Table)

	<u>Employees</u>		<u>Self-employed and</u> <u>other non-employees</u>	
<u>Fatal injury</u>	<u>Major injury</u>	<u>Fatal injury</u>	<u>Major injury</u>
471	12,290	132	5,749

<u>Source</u>: HSC Report 1983-1984: data corrected in November 1984 (HMSO)

APPENDIX 3

HEALTH AND SAFETY AT WORK ETC ACT 1974: INSTRUMENTS MADE UNDER
PARTS I AND IV RELEVANT TO HSC/E RESPONSIBILITIES

1. The Health and Safety at Work etc Act 1974 (Commencement No 1) Order 1974 No 1439 (Spent)

2. The Anthrax Prevention Act 1919 (Repeals and Modifications) Regulations 1974 No 1775

3. The Factories Act 1961 (Enforcement of Section 135) Regulations 1974 No 1776

4. The Docks and Harbours Act 1966 (Modification) Regulations 1974 No 1820

5. The Radioactive Substances Act 1948 (Modification) Regulations 1974 No 1821

6. The Hydrogen Cyanide (Fumigation) Act 1937 (Repeals and Modifications) Regulations 1974 No 1840

7. The Celluloid and Cinematograph Film Act 1922 (Repeals and Modifications) Regulations 1974 No 1841

8. The Explosives Acts 1875 and 1923 etc (Repeals and Modifications) Regulations 1974 No 1885

9. The Boiler Explosions Acts 1882 and 1890 (Repeals and Modifications) Regulation 1974 No 1886 (Revoked by SI 1980 No 804)

10. The Truck Acts 1831 to 1896 (Enforcement) Regulations 1974 No 1887

11. The Industrial Tribunals (Improvement and Prohibition Notices Appeals) Regulations 1974 No 1925

12. The Industrial Tribunals (Improvement and Prohibition Notices Appeals) (Scotlan Regulations 1974 No 1926

13. The Factories Act 1961 etc (Repeals and Modifications) Regulations 1974 No 1941

14. The Petroleum (Regulation) Acts 1928 and 1936 (Repeals and Modifications) Regulations 1974 No 1942

15. The Offices, Shops and Railway Premises Act 1963 (Repeals and Modifications) Regulations 1974 No 1943

16. The Pipe-lines Act 1962 (Repeals and Modifications) Regulations 1974 No 1986

17. The Coal Industry Nationalisation Act 1946 (Repeals) Regulations 1974 No 2011

18. The Ministry of Fuel and Power Act 1945 (Repeal) Regulations 1974 No 2012

19. The Mines and Quarries Acts 1954 to 1971 (Repeals and Modifications) Regulations 1974 No 2013

20. The Health and Safety Licensing Appeals (Hearings Procedure) Rules 1974 No 2040

21. The Nuclear Installations Act 1965 etc (Repeals and Modifications)
Regulations 1974 No 2056

22. The Health and Safety Licensing Appeals (Hearings Procedure) (Scotland) Rules
1974 No 2068

23. The Explosives Acts 1875 and 1923 etc (Repeals and Modifications (Amendment)
Regulations 1974 No 2166

24. Clean Air Enactments (Repeals and Modifications) Regulations 1974 No 2170

25. The Agriculture (Poisonous Substances) Act 1952 (Repeals and Modification)
Regulations 1975 No 45

26. The Agriculture (Safety, Health and Welfare Provisions) Act 1956 (Repeals and
Modifications) Regulations 1975 No 46

27. The Health and Safety (Agriculture)(Poisonous Substances) Regulations 1975 No
282 Revoked by SI 1984 No 1114.

28. The Protection of Eyes (Amendment) Regulations 1975 No 303

29. The Health and Safety Inquiries (Procedure) Regulations 1975 No 335

30. The Offices, Shops and Railway Premises Act 1963 (Repeals) Regulations 1975
No 1011

31. The Factories Act 1961 (Repeals) Regulations 1975 No 1012

32. The Mines and Quarries Acts 1954 to 1971 (Repeals and Modifications) Regulations
1975 No 1102

33. The Coal Mines (Respirable Dust) Regulations 1975 No 1433

34. The Employers' Health and Safety Policy Statements (Exception) Regulations 1975
No 1584

35. The Conveyance of Explosives by Road (Special Case) Regulations 1975 No 1621
(Spent)

36 The Baking and Sausage Making (Christmas and New Year) Regulations 1975
No 1695 (Spent)

37. The Coal and Mines (Precuations against Inflammable Dust) Temporary Provisions
Regulations 1976 No 881 (Spent)

38. The Operations at Unfenced Machinery (Amendment) Regulations 1976 No 955

39. The Health and Safety Inquiries (Procedure) (Amendment) Regulations 1976 No 1246

40. The Health and Safety (Agriculture) (Miscellaneous Repeals and Modifications)
Regulations 1976 No 1247

41. The Baking and Sausage Making (Christmas and New Year) Regulations 1976
No 1908 (Spent)

42 The Fire Certificates (Special Premises) Regulations 1976 No 2003

43. The Factories Act 1961 etc (Repeals) Regulations 1976 No 2004

44. The Offices, Shops and Railway Premises Act 1963 etc (Repeals) Regulations 1976 No 2005

45. The Fire Precautions Act 1971 (Modifications) Regulations 1976 No 2007

46. The Mines and Quarries (Metrication) Regulations 1976 No 2063

47. The Safety Representatives and Safety Committees Regulations 1977 No 500

48. The Health and Safety (Enforcing Authority) Regulations 1977 No 746

49. The Coal Mines (Precautions against Inflammable Dust) Amendment Regulations 1977 No 913

50. The Explosives (Registration of Premises) Variation of Fees Regulations 1977 No 918 (Revoked by SI 1983 No 219)

51. The Coal and Other Mines (Electricity) (Third Amendment) Regulations 1977 No 1205

52. The Health and Safety at work etc Act 1974 (Application outside Great Britain) Order 1977 No 1232

53. The Acetylene (Exemption) Order 1977 No 1798 (Spent)

54. The Baking and Sausage Making (Christmas and New Year) Regulations 1977 No 1841 (Spent)

55. The Packaging and Labelling of Dangerous Substances Regulations 1978 No 209 (Revoked by SI 1984 No 1244)

56. The Explosives (Licensing of Stores) Variation of Fees Regulations 1978 No 270 (Revoked by SI 1983 No 219)

57. The Petroleum (Regulation) Acts 1928 and 1936 (Variation of Fees) Regulations 1978 No 635 (Revoked by SI 1981 No 1333)

58. the Health and Safety (Genetic Manipulation) Regulations 1978 No 752

59. The Coal Mines (Respirable Dust) (Amendment) Regulations 1978 No 807

60. The Factories (Standards of Lighting) (Revocation) Regulations 1978 No 1126

61. The Baking and Sausage Making (Christmas and New Year) Regulations 1978 No 1516 (Spent)

62. The Coal and Other Mines (Metrication) Regulations 1978 No 1648

63. The Hazardous Substances (Labelling of Road Tankers) Regulations 1978 No 1702 (Revoked by SI 1981 No 1059)

64. The Compressed Acetylene (Importation) Regulations 1978 No 1723

65. The Mines and Quarries Act 1954 (Modification) Regulations 1978 No 1951

66. The Mines (Precautions Against Inrushes) Regulations 1979 No 318

67. The Petroleum (Consolidation) Act 1928 (Enforcement) Regulations 1979 No 427

68. The Coal and Other Mines (Electric Lighting for Filming) Regulations 1979 No 1203

69. The Baking and Sausage Making (Christmas and New Year) Regulations 1979 No 1298 (Spent)

70. The Explosives Act 1875 (Exemptions) Regulations 1979 No 1378

71. The Health and Safety (Fees for Medical Examinations) Regulations 1979 No 1553 (Revoked by SI 1981 No 334)

72. The Notification of Accidents and Dangerous Occurrences Regulations 1980 No 804

73. The Health and Safety (Leasing Arrangements) Regulations 1980 No 907

74. The Coal and Other Mines (Fire and Rescue) (Amendment) Regulations 1980 No 942

75. The Agriculture (Tractor Cabs) (Amendment) Regulations 1980 No 1036 (Revoked by SI 1984 No 605)

76. The Petroleum (Consolidation) Act 1928 (Conveyance by Road Regulations Exemptions) Regulations 1980 No 1100

77. The Mines and Quarries (Fees for Approvals) Regulations 1980 No 1233

78. The Control of Lead at Work Regulations 1980 No 1248

79. The Celluloid and Cinematograph Film Act 1922 (Exemptions) Regulations 1980 No 1314

80. The Safety Signs Regulations 1980 No 1471

81. The Baking and Sausage Making (Christmas and New Year) Regulations 1980 No 1576. (Spent)

82. The Health and Safety (Animal Products) (Metrication) Regulations 1980 No 1690

83. The Health and Safety (Enforcing Authority) (Amendment) Regulations 1980 No 1744

84. The Chemical Works (Metrication) Regulations 1981 No 16

85. The Mines and Quarries (Fees for Approvals) (Amendment) Regulations 1981 No 270 (Revoked by SI 1982 No 247)

86. The Health and Safety (Fees for Medical Examinations) Regulations 1981 No 334 (Revoked by SI 1983 No 714)

87. The Diving Operations at Work Regulations 1981 No 399

88. The Aerated Water Regulations (Metrication) Regulations 1981 No 686

89. The Gasholders and Steam Boilers Regulations (Metrication) Regulations 1981 No 687

90. The Pipe-lines Act 1962 (Metrication) Regulations 1981 No 695

91. The Packaging and Labelling of Dangerous Substances (Amendment) Regulations 198
No 792 (Revoked by SI 1984 No 1244)

92. The Health and Safety (First-Aid) Regulations 1981 No 917

93. The Health and Safety (Dangerous Pathogens) Regulations 1981 No 1011

94. The Dangerous Substances (Conveyance by Road in Road Tankers and Tank Container
Regulations 1981 No 1059

95. The Kiers Regulations 1938 (Metrication) Regulations 1981 No 1152

96. The Locomotives etc Regulations 1906 (Metrication) Regulations 1981 No 1327

97. The Health and Safety (Foundries etc) (Metrication) Regulations
1981 No 1332

98. The Petroleum (Regulation) Acts 1928 and 1936 (Fees) Regulations 1981 No 1333
(Revoked by SI 1983 No. 1640)

99. The Agriculture (Metrication) Regulations 1981 No 1414

100. The Grinding of Metals etc (Metrication) Regulations 1981 No 1486

101. The Baking and Sausage Making (Christmas and New Year) Regulations 1981
No 1498 (Spent)

102. The Petroleum (Regulation) Acts 1928 and 1936 (Fees) (Amendment) Regulations
1981 No 1652 (Revoked by SI 1983 No. 1640)

103. The Mines and Quarries (Fees for Approval) (Amendment) Regulations 1982 No 247
(Revoked by SI 1983 No 484)

104. The Petroleum-Spirit (Plastic Containers) Regulations 1982 No 630

105. The Hydrogen Cyanide (Fumigation of Buildings) (Amendment) Regulations 1982 No
695

106. The Offices, Shops and Railway Premises Act 1963 etc (Metrication) Regulations
1982 No 827

107. The Pottery (Health etc) (Metrication) Regulations 1982 No 877

108. The Notification of Installations Handling Hazardous Substances Regulations
1982 No 1357

109. The Anthrax Prevention Order 1971 (Exemptions) Regulations, 1982 No 1418

110. The Notification of New Substances Regulations 1982 No 1496

111. The Baking and Sausage Making (Christmas and New Year) Regulations 1982
No 1503 (Spent)

112. The Packaging and Labelling of Dangerous Substances (Amendment) Regulations 198
No 17 (Revoked by SI 1984 No 1244)

113. The Health and Safety (Miscelleneous Fees for Approvals) Regulations 1983 No 70

114. The Explosives (Licensing of Stores and Registration of Premises) Fees Regulations 1983 No 219 •

115. The Mines and Quarries (Fees for Approvals) (Amendment) Regulations 1983 No 484 (Revoked by SI 1984 No 310)

116. Dock, Shipbuilding etc (Metrication) Regulations 1983 No. 644

117. The Coal and Other Mines (Safety-Lamps and Lighting) (Amendment) Regulations 1983 No 710

118. The Health and Safety (Fees for Medical Examinations) Regulations 1983 No. 714 (Revoked by SI 1984 No 569)

119. Health and Safety (Emissions into the Atmosphere) Regulations 1983 No 943

120. The Dry Cleaning (Metrication) Regulations 1983 No. 977

121. The Factories Act 1961 etc (Metrication) Regulations 1983 No 978

122. The Factories (Testing of Aircraft Engines and Accessories) (Metrication) Regulations 1983 No 979

123. The Miscellaneous Mines (Metrication) Regulations 1983 No 994

124. The Quarries (Metrication) Regulations 1983 No 1026

125. Mines (Miscellaneous Amendments) Regulations 1983 No 1130

126. The Classification and Labelling of Explosives Regulations 1983 No 1140

127. The Explosives and Related Matters (Fees) Regulation 1983 No 1450

128. Baking and Sausage Making (Christmas New Year) Regulations 1983 No 1502 (Spent)

129. The Hoists and Lifts (Metrication) Regulations 1983 No 1579

130. The Petroleum (Regulations) Acts 1928 and 1936 (Fees) Regulations 1983 No. 1640

131. Asbestos (Licensing) Regulations 1983 No. 1649

132. The Health and Safety (Youth Training Scheme) Regulations 1983 No 1919

133. The Mines and Quarries (Fees for Approvals) (Amendment) Regulation 1984 No 310

134. The Explosives Act 1875 etc. (Metrication and Miscellenous Amendment) Regulations 1984 No. 510

135. The Health and Safety (Fees for Medical Examinations) Regulations 1984 No 569 (Revoked by SI 1985 No 279)

136. The Agriculture (Tractor Cabs) (Amendment) Regulation 1984 No 605

137. The Poisonous Substances in Agricure Regulations 1984 No 114

138. The Classification, Packaging and Labelling of Dangerous Substances Regulations 1984 No. 1244

139. The Construction (Metrication) Regulations 1984 No 1593

140. The Baking and Sausage Making (Christmas and New Year) Regulations 1984 No 1598
     Spent

141. The Freight Containers (Safety Convention) Regulations 1984 No 1890

142. The Control of Industrial Major Accidents Hazards Regulations 1984 No 1902

143. The Health and Safety (Fees for Medical Examinations) Regulations 1985 No 279

LIST OF APPROVED CODES OF PRACTICE ISSUED UNDER SECTION 16 OF THE HEALTH AND SAFETY AT WORK ETC ACT 1974

1. Safety representatives and safety committees (in support of SI 1977 No 500): brown booklet.

2. Time off for the training of Safety Representatives (in support of SI 1977 No 500): leaflet HSC 9.

3. Control of lead at work (in support of SI 1980 No 1248): unnumbered booklet.

4. Work with asbestos insulation and asbestos coating (in support of SI 1969 No 690 and the general duties of the HSW Act 1974): booklet COP 3. (Revised June 1983 to take effect 1st August 1983).

5. Health and Safety (First-Aid) Regulations 1981: booklet COP 4.

6. Classification of dangerous substances for conveyance in road tankers and tank containers (in support of SI 1981 No. 1059): booklet COP 5.

7. Petroleum-Spirit (Plastic Containers) Regulations 1982. Requirements for testing and marking or labelling (in support of SI 1982 No. 630) booklet COP 6.

8. Principles of good laboratory practice. Notification of New Substances Regulation 1982 (in support of SI 1982 No. 1496): booklet COP 7.

9. Methods for the determination of ecotoxicity. Notification of New Substances Regulations 1982 (in support of SI 1982 No. 1496): booklet COP 8.

10. Methods for the determination of physico - chemical properties. Notification of New Substances Regulations 1982 (in support of SI 1982 No 1496): booklet COP 9

11. Methods for the determination of toxicity. Notification of New Substances Regulations 1982 (in support of SI 1982 No. 1496): booklet COP 10.

12. British Standards BS 697 1977 "Specification for Rubber Gloves for Electrical purposes"

13. British Standard BS 1870 Part 1: 1979 "Specification for Safety Footwear other than all-rubber and all-plastic moulded types".

14. British Standard BS 5426: 1976 "Specification for Workwear".

15. British Standard BS 5169: 1975 "Specification for Fusion welded steel air receivers".

16. Operational provisions of the Dangerous Substances (Conveyance by road in Road Tankers and Tank Containers) Regulations 1981.

17. British Standard BS 1870 Part 2:1976 Specification for lined Rubber Safety Boots.

18. British Standard BS 1870 Part 3: 1981 Specification for Polyvinyl Chloride Moulded Safety Footwear.

19   Packaging of dangerous substances for conveyance by road
        Classification, Packaging and Labelling of Dangerous Substances
        Regulations 1984 in support of SI 1982 No 1496 and SI 1984 No 1244
        unnumbered booklet.

20   Classification and labelling of substances dangerous for supply and/or
        conveyance by road.
        Notification of New Substances Regulations 1982.
        Classification, Packaging and Labelling of Dangerous
        Substances Regulations 1984.

        (in support of SI 1982 No 1496 and SI 1984 No 1244) unnumbered booklet.

APPENDIX 4

List of prescribed diseases and the occupations for which they are prescribed

Disease No.	Prescribed disease or injury	Type of occupation Any occupation involving
	A. CONDITIONS DUE TO PHYSICAL AGENTS (physical cause)	
A1 Previously 25	Inflammation, ulceration or malignant disease of the skin or subcutaneous tissues or of the bones, or blood dyserasia, or cataract, due to electro-magnetic radiations (other than radiant heat), or to ionising particles. Radiation diseases. e.g. certain kinds of leukaemia due to exposure to radiation at work.	Exposure to electro-magnetic radiations (other than radiant heat) to ionising particles. e.g. workers exposed to radiation in the nuclear fuel and power industry, hospital X-ray departments.
A2 Previously 26	Heat Cataract. Disease of the eye.	Frequent or prolonged exposure to rays from molten or red-hot material. e.g. underwater or tunnel workers.
A3 Previously 27 rarefied other gases	Dysbarism, including de-compression sickness, bar otrauma and osteonecro-sis. e.g. The Bends.	Subjection to compressed or rarefied air or other respirable gases or gaseous mixtures. e.g. underwater or tunnel-workers.
A4 Previously 27 or	Cramp of the hand or fore-arm due to repetitive movements. e.g. Writer's cramp.	Prolonged periods of handwriting, typing or other repetitive movements of the fingers, hand or arm. e.g. typists, clerks and routine assemblers.

A5 Previously 31	Subcutaneous cellulitis of the hand. (Beat hand)	Manual labour causing severe or prolonged friction or pressure on the hand. e.g. miners and road workers using picks and shovels.
A6 Previously 32	Bursitis or subcutaneous cellulitis arising at or about the knee due to severe or prolonged external friction or pressure at or about the knee. (Beat knee). e.g. Housemaid's knee.	Manual labour causing severe or prolonged pressure at or about the e.g. workers who kneel a lot.
A7 Previously 33	Bursitis or subcutaneous cellulitis arising at or about the elbow due to severe or prolonged external friction or pressure at or about the elbow. (Beat elbow)	Manual labour causing severe or prolonged external friction or pressure at or about the elbow. e.g. jobs involving continuous rubbing or pressure on the elbow.
A8 Previously 34	Traumatic inflammation of the tendons of the hand or forearm, or of the associated tendon sheaths. Tenosyonovitis.	Manual labour, or frequent or repeated movements of the hand or wrist. e.g. routine assembly workers.
A9 Previously 35	Miner's nystagmus. Jerky movements of the eyeballs.	Work in or about a mine.
A10 Previously 48	Occupational deafness.	(See leaflet Nl.207 for details)
	B. CONDITIONS DUE TO BIOLOGICAL AGENTS (caused by animal, plant or other living organism.	
B1 Previously 19	Anthrax	Contact with animals infected with anthrax or the handling (including the loading or unloading or transport) of animal products or residues. e.g. glue and shaving brush makers.

B2 Previously 20	Glanders	Contact with equine animals or their carcasses. e.g. farm and slaughter house workers and grooms handling horses.
B3 Previously 21	Infection by Leptospira. e.g. swamp fever, swine-herd's disease, and Well's disease.	(a) Work in places which are, or are liable to be, infested by rats, field mice or voles, or other small mammals; or (b) work at dog kennels or the care or handling of dogs; or (c) contact with bovine animals or their meat products or pigs or their meat products. e.g. farm, veterinary, sewerage and slaughter house workers.
B4 Previously 22	Ankylostomiasis Hookworm disease - rarely found in this country.	Work in or about a mine.
B5	Tuberculosis TB.	Contact with a source of tuberculous infection. e.g. doctors, nurses, ambulance crews, pathology technicians and social workers.
B6 Previously 43	Extrinsic allergic alveolitis (including Farmer's lung).	Exposure to moulds of fungal spores or heterologous proteins by reason of employment in: (a) agriculture, horticulture, forestry, cultivation of edible fungi or maltworking; or (b) loading or unloading or handling in storage mouldy vegetable matter or edible fungi; or (c) caring for or handling birds; or (d) handling bagasse.

B7 Previously 46	Infection by organisms of the genus brucella. Brucellosis.	Contact with: (a) animals infected by brucella, or their carcasses or parts thereof, or their un-treated products; of (b) laboratory specimens or vaccines of, or containing, brucella. e.g. farm, veterinary, slaughter house, animal laboratory workers.
B8 Previously 49	Viral hepatitus. An infection of the liver by a virus.	Contact with: (a) human blood or human blood produocts; or (b) a source of viral hepatitis. e.g. doctors, nurses, ambulance crews, pathology workers.
B9 Newly described	Infection by streptococcus suis. A very rare from of meningitis from exposure to infected pigs or pork products;	Contact with pigs infected by streptococcus suis, or with the carcasses, products or residues of pigs so infected. e.g. pork butchers, pig breeders, slaughter house workers.
C. CONDITIONS DUE TO CHEMICAL AGENTS (Chemical cause)		
C1 Previously 1	Poisoning by lead or a compound of lead.	The use or handling of, or exposure to the fumes, dust or vapour of, lead or a compound of lead, or a substance containing lead. e.g. plumbers, painters, enamellers, pottery glazing workers.
C2 Previously 2	Poisoning by manganese or a compound of manganese.	The use or handling of, or exposure to the fumes, dust or vapour of, manganese, or a substance containing manganese. e.g. dry battery, pottery glazing and soap workers.

C3 Previously 3, 11 and 12	Poisoning by phosphorus or an inorganic compound of phosphorus or poisoning due to the anti-cholinesterase or pseudo anti-cholinesterase action of organic phosphorus compounds.	The use or handling of, or exposure to the fumes, dust or vapour of phosphorus or a compound of phosphorus, or a substance containing phosphorus. e.g. pest control, agricultural workers, workers on incendiary devices, match makers.
C4 Previously 4	Poisoning by arsenic or a compound of arsenic	The use or handling of, or exposure to the fumes, dust or vapour of arsenic or a compound of arsenic, or a substance containing arsenic. e.g. leather, agricultural and metal pickling workers.
C5 Previously 5	Poisoning by mercury or a compound of mercury.	The use or handling of, or exposure to the fumes, dust or vapour of m⁻rcury, or a substance containing mercury. e.g. mirror/thermometer makers, market gardeners and explosives workers.
C6 Previously	Poisoning by carbon bisulphide.	The use of handling of, or exposure to the fumes or vapour of, carbon bisulphide or a compound of carbon bisulphide, or a substance containing carbon bisulphide. e.g. artificial silk and cellophane makers, rubber vulcanisers.
C7 Previously 7	Poisoning by benzene or a homologue of benzene. Benzol/benzole, toluene/toluol, xylene/xytol.	The use or handling of, or exposure to the fumes of, or vapour containing benzene or any of its homolugues. e.g. paint, dye, rubber goods and artificial leather workers.
C8 Previously 8	Poisoning by a nitro- or amino- or choloro-derivative of benzene or of benzene or of a homologue of benzene, or poisoning by nitrochlor-benzene. e.g. Tri-nitro-toluene (TNT)	